Abraham J. Twerski, M.D., is the Medical Director of Gateway Rehabilitation Center and Clinical Director, Department of Psychiatry, St. Francis General Hospital, Pittsburgh, Pennsylvania. He is an ordained Rabbi and Assistant Professor of Psychiatry, University of Pittsburgh School of Medicine. He is the author of two other books available from Prentice Hall Press.

Books by Abraham J. Twerski, M.D.

LIKE YOURSELF* *AND OTHERS WILL, TOO (1978)

CAUTION: "KINDNESS" CAN BE DANGEROUS TO THE ALCOHOLIC (1981)

WHO SAYS YOU'RE NEUROTIC? (1984)

CAUTION

"Kindness" Can Be Dangerous to the Alcoholic

Abraham J. Twerski, M.D.

PRENTICE HALL PRESS • NEW YORK

This book is available at a special discount when ordered in large quantities. Contact Prentice Hall Press, Reference Group Special Sales, 13th floor, 1 Gulf + Western Plaza, New York, NY 10023

Published in 1987 by Prentice Hall Press
A Division of Simon & Schuster, Inc.
Gulf + Western Building
One Gulf + Western Plaza
New York, NY 10023

Originally published by Prentice-Hall, Inc.

Library of Congress Cataloging-in-Publication Data

Twerski, Abraham J.
Caution, "kindness" can be dangerous to the alcoholic.

Bibliography: p.
Includes index.
1. Alcoholism. 2. Alcoholics—Family relationships.
3. Alcoholism—Treatment. I. Title.
HV5275.T87 362.2'928 81-605
ISBN 0-13-121244-3 AACR2
ISBN 0-13-121236-2 (pbk.)

Manufactured in the United States of America

7 8 9 10 11 12 13 14 15

First Prentice Hall Press Edition

Contents

Preface

It is extremely frustrating to know that one is going to be misunderstood and misquoted, that in spite of efforts at clarification, intended meanings will be distorted. It is even more exasperating when such distortion is apt to result in the polar opposite of what was intended.

For instance, I wish to state categorically that *no one in the environment is responsible for the drinking of anyone else*. Husbands are not responsible for their wives' drinking, and wives are not responsible for their husbands' drinking. Nor are employers responsible for their employees' drinking, and vice versa. Obviously, people who interrelate can provoke feelings of anxiety, tension, hostility, or envy in one another, but the decision to drink away these or any other uncomfortable feelings is *no one else's but the alcoholic's*. As will be pointed out, this decision is a sick decision, and the issue of "responsibility" for a decision emanating from an illness that distorts judgment and insight is difficult to delineate both morally and legally.

Yet, because this book discusses the ways in which

those other persons in the environment of the alcoholic inadvertently support the drinking instead of doing those things that would tend to bring the problem to an end, some people are going to conclude that what I am saying is that those in the alcoholic's environment are responsible for his drinking. This is a totally false and erroneous conclusion.

Let us take an analogy. Fire cannot burn in the absence of oxygen, but all the oxygen in the world will not *cause* a fire. The fire is caused by someone or something igniting the flame. True, once the fire is burning, it can be extinguished if the flame is smothered so that oxygen does not reach it, but obviously, we would not say that oxygen *causes* the fire.

Although this analogy may not be precise, it does convey the general idea. The alcoholic would like nothing better than to point at the spouse, in-laws, employer, job, or business associates, and hold them responsible for the drinking. For less-well-understood reasons, the people in the environment of the alcoholic may hold themselves responsible for the drinking. *This is not true.* Cutting out the support system for the drinking may have a salutory effect, just as eliminating the oxygen supply will extinguish the flame, but the support system should not be seen as the *cause* of the drinking.

Rarely, if ever, is the alcoholic actually encouraged to drink, and almost never is the support system operating out of malice. Sometimes the support system exists out of self-serving interests among those in the alcoholic's environment, and very often there is actually a benevolent intent among those who would like to "help." What is not sufficiently appreciated are those situations where benevolence can often be harmful. The mother who does not immunize her infant against serious illnesses because she does not want to inflict the pain of the hypodermic needle or have the baby get a reaction to the innoculation is manifesting a very shortsighted and ill-fated benevolence. The infant, who lacks the capacity to choose the innoculation, is totally dependent on the mother to take the appropriate steps to prevent his succumbing to tetanus. The alcoholic, who in his addiction is blind to his condition, is essentially dependent upon those close to him to see what is going on, and to take the necessary steps to prevent the process from causing his doom.

In the following pages, illustrative cases and theoretical considerations will be presented to help those other persons relating to the alcoholic realize that what appears to be kindness and concern for the drinker are often misguided efforts. Since those relating to the alcoholic include the employer, physician, clergyman, and counselor, as well as family members, this book is addressed to all concerned. It was very difficult to avoid repetition of some principles and suggestions valid to all in the chapters dealing with specific relationships. I do not wish to apologize too much for repetition, since in this most difficult field of human suffering, some things cannot be said often enough.

The reader may be somewhat confused about my attitude toward the alcoholic and the family. At times it appears to be punitive, in some places it may appear to be callous, and yet the underlying theme is one of care, concern, sympathy, and empathy. How can such conflicting attitudes coexist in one person?

As an explanation, I would like to invoke the analogy of the parent-child relationship. Like any parent who loved and cared for his children, I found it necessary at times to actually inflict pain on my child when I felt it to be for his welfare. When the child was an infant, I had to restrain him while the pediatrician examined him in ways which appeared to be most unpleasant, such as administering a painful jab of the hypodermic needle. Perhaps it seemed callous when I gave up my repeated attempts to prevent him from touching the hot radiator and finally said, "Okay, son, find out for yourself how hot it is." There were a number of times when I had to inflict what I felt to be requisite punishment. Yet, all of these emanated from sincere love and concern for my child's welfare. Indeed, had someone else dared lay a hand on my child, I would have immediately come to his defense. *My* spanking was an outgrowth of my sense of responsibility for the child's development, and the manifest love I bestowed upon my child by far overshadowed the occasional disciplinary actions. Anyone else, who did not have this love for him, had no right to cause him any unpleasantness.

I recall the case of a woman who was repeatedly admitted to the hospital for "drying out." My investigation revealed that she had never followed through with the recommended after-care plan, and it became evident to me that she allowed herself to drink to excess partly because she knew that when she became sick as a result of her drinking, she could come to Twerski and he would help her feel better. I had become a part of her addiction support system!

Prior to her discharge from the hospital, I advised the woman that unless she followed instructions for outpatient treatment, I would refuse to re-admit her. I then left instructions in the emergency room that if she reappeared there intoxicated, I was to be called personally, regardless of whether or not I was on call at the time.

The call came three weeks later at 1:00 A.M. I could have refused her admission over the phone, but instead I got out of bed, dressed, and drove down to the hospital. In spite of her entreaties, I was adamant in refusing to admit her, and I sent her away from the emergency room. I spent the rest of the night sleepless with worry about where she might be, and the following morning I called some of her acquaintances to go check on her.

There is a difference between sending an intoxicated person away from the emergency room for reasons described above, or rejecting him because "we don't admit drunks." I have no sympathy for hospitals who refuse to taint their lily-white hands with intoxicated persons. Perhaps the best test is: If you don't feel hurt and worried when you turn the alcoholic away, you have no right to do so.

It is little wonder that the woman in the above case has now been sober for four years. The message communicated itself very well: the refusal was born of concern, not contempt.

To extend the parent-child analogy further, the parent's love for the infant does not necessitate the delusion that one loves foul-smelling, messy diapers. One can very well loathe the filthy diaper without at all diminishing one's love for the child. Similarly, there is no need to pretend that intoxicated behavior is not repulsive and obnoxious, and can provoke anger and irritation. Yet, despising drunkenness need not carry over into dislike of the alcoholic.

The chapters that follow essentially elaborate and clarify one central theme. *In virtually all instances, there is nothing that you can do to change the alcoholic. All that you can do is to stop the kind of behavior that prevents the alcoholic from feeling the impact of destructive drinking soon enough to save himself or herself, and, it is hoped, preserve the family unit.*

It is my sincere hope that among the countless number of people negatively affected by someone's pathologic drinking, some will be sufficiently open-minded and give consideration to observations and suggestions resulting from years of involvement with thousands of alcoholics and their families.

A Dedication

As a first-year psychiatric resident, I was assigned to the walk-in clinic. One day a woman came in asking for help. The woman gave the high points of her history. When she was twenty-four, married, and with a baby, she was drinking so heavily that her husband asked for a divorce. Recognizing that she was not fulfilling her functions as a wife and mother, she gave her husband the divorce and custody of the child. Free of all restraints, she now indulged in alcohol even more heavily.

Even at sixty-one, when I first met her, Isabel was an attractive woman. She must have been stunning in her younger years, when she was much sought after as a companion, being wined and dined by the social élite. As the years went on and alcohol took its toll, Isabel's social life deteriorated drastically. Between the ages of thirty and fifty-seven, she had more than 65 hospitalizations for "drying out." Her behavior had become so intolerable that her family eventually detached themselves completely from her, even refusing to respond to calls from the hospital. She made several token visits to Alcoholics Anonymous (AA), but she never took the program seriously. Eventually she ended up in the skid-row flophouses.

At age fifty-seven, Isabel called a lawyer who had extricated her from many difficulties and asked him for a favor.

"What is it this time?" the lawyer asked.

"I want you to put me away in the state hospital for a year," Isabel answered. (At that time, the state Inebriate Act provided for commitment for a period of one year for alcoholism.)

"You don't know what you're saying," the lawyer said. But as Isabel persisted, he suggested, "Think it over a while. If you still want it, I'll do it for you."

One week later, Isabel again asked for commitment to the state hospital, which the lawyer then arranged. After the year of hospitalization was over, Isabel joined AA and took a job as a housekeeper.

At the time she consulted me, Isabel had been sober for four years. Her attempts to recontact her family had all been rejected. I was unable to determine just what it was that she was seeking in psychiatric help, but her story fascinated me. Obviously there had to be a motivating factor for her becoming sober and remaining sober even after being rejected by her family. Just what did she have to gain by becoming sober? Although I did not see any need for treatment, I encouraged Isabel to return so that I could discover the reason for her sobriety.

Having learned nothing about alcoholism in medical school nor in my psychiatric training, I had assumed, like many others, that alcoholism cannot be treated. As the sessions with Isabel continued, I became aware of the workings of AA and sufficiently curious to attend the meetings of this group of people who treated a condition in ways of which medicine was apparently ignorant. The more I attended AA, the more I found that its basic philosophy is applicable to management of stress, even when alcohol is not involved.

As Clinical Director of the Department of Psychiatry of Pittsburgh's St. Francis General Hospital, I was detoxifying about 900 cases of alcoholism annually. The need for a local rehabilitation center was grossly evident, and in 1972 the Gateway Rehabilitation Center, essentially a monument to Isabel, was opened.

Isabel's motivation for sobriety continued to elude me, and although I continued to see her until her death at seventy-four, I never did discover any specific reason for her turning her life around. All I can conclude is that within every person there is a nucleus of self-respect and dignity which, no matter how deeply concealed, exists obstinately. There comes a time when a person discovers that he dare not be anything less than that which he can be, and at such a time, the miracle of sobriety can occur.

This was a long way of saying that this book is dedicated to Isabel.

1

Unhelpful Help

Case 1

The phone rang. "Doctor, what can I do about my husband? His drinking is just terrible. He is ruining himself and me and everything he ever worked for."

I asked the woman whether her husband was willing to come in for help. "Oh no," she said. "He doesn't think there is anything wrong with him. He says he only drinks beer, so he can't be alcoholic."

I advised the woman that unless her husband was interested in coming for help, there was nothing we could do. "Could I bring him in by ambulance when he drinks himself into a stupor?" she asked. I told her that although this was technically possible, it would serve no practical purpose, because he would be able to pick himself up and leave the hospital as soon as he awoke.

"But certainly there must be something I can do," she insisted. "I can't just stand by and see him destroy himself." I then suggested to the wife that she come to the meeting of family members of persons having problems with alcohol that we would be holding later in the week.

At the meeting, the woman described her plight. Her husband was a professional person, now in his mid-fifties. Although he had for many years drunk to excess, there had never been any interference with his work. Within the past year, however, the pattern had changed significantly. The weekend drinking had become so heavy that he could not function well enough to work in the office on Mondays. Then Wednesday afternoon became an off-day, and the weekend would begin on Friday morning. Gradually his work degenerated to the point where the office had to be closed. For the past several months, his life consisted of lying on the couch watching television and consuming beer by the case.

One of the group members inquired how she was now supporting herself since her husband was obviously not earning anything. "Well, I am a registered nurse," the wife said. "I do private-duty nursing. Our two children are married, and I can makè enough to keep the house going for both of us, although it is quite a tight squeeze." The group then pointed out to her that under the circumstances, there was no pressure to motivate her husband toward change. Regardless of what might have led to his drinking, he was now in a tolerable if not comfortable niche. He was staying home, resting and watching television, tranquilizing himself with beer, while she was out working to pay the rent.

The woman insisted that her husband must be made to recognize how far he had deteriorated. The group advised her that she could not expect him to change on his own, particularly since she was actually enabling him to continue his drinking by supporting him. Someone suggested that if she indeed believed that alcohol was destroying him, she should stop participating in his addiction to alcohol; she should find herself a small apartment, and leave him a note: "Dear, I have decided that I cannot live a destructive life of alcohol. If you must live this way, you may get on welfare or find some other way to support yourself." The wife rejected this advice. "How could I walk out on him now? Just think of what that might do to him."

Case 2

A young woman of twenty was admitted to the hospital because of addiction to narcotics. While in high school, she had begun using various drugs, including LSD, sleeping pills, "speed," alcohol, and narcotics, developing a habit of progressive severity.

Following her admission, an interview with her parents was held. They were shocked to learn of her drug and alcohol problem, stating that they had never suspected anything of the sort. Although she had been away at school for two years, she had been using various chemicals and alcohol extensively before that time, and I pointed out to the parents that they must have been aware of some unusual behavior. They persisted in their denial of such recognition.

I learned from the parents that they had been sending their daughter substantial sums of money while she was away at school, and I pointed out to them that she had obviously used this money to finance her drug habit. At this time, the patient was intending to return to school immediately after discharge from the hospital, and I advised the parents that there was a very high probability that she would soon revert to the use of drugs. The parents were horrified and stated that they would do anything within their power to stop her addiction.

I told the parents that there was pathetically little that they could do and that recovery depended upon the patient's motivation, but they could at least refrain from supporting the continuation of the habit. I suggested that they arrange to pay their daughter's room and board directly, have her buy her clothes and most of her necessities at home, and give her a minimum of pocket money. In this way, they would not be accomplices to her addiction by underwriting its support.

The parents agreed to this advice. I then spent some time discussing with them the disastrous consequences of addiction, pointing out that it was unquestionably self-destructive. They fully concurred with this statement. At this point, I asked, "Now, what would happen if you were to discover that your daughter resumed using drugs, but because you had cut off the money supply she had turned to prostitution to keep her habit going?" The mother was shaken. "Oh my God!" she said, "I would send her the money."

Case 3

Carol is a thirty-nine-year-old housewife, mother of two children. She had developed an alcohol problem of extreme magnitude, and her behavior was destroying the household. She would drink herself to sleep, get up at 4:00 a.m. and drink again, and was still asleep when the children had to be sent to school. Her behavior at social events had been so disgraceful that her husband refused to take her to places where alcohol might be served. He had tried to control her consumption by getting rid of all alcohol in the house, but she was able to procure it and hide it in places he would never discover.

At one point, Carol was deeply hurt when she overheard her ten-year-old son tell a friend on the phone that he could not invite him over to his home; his father had said that they should not bring friends over, since they might see what their mother looked like and the story would get out. Carol then decided that she would not drink anymore, and she went through several days of severe nervousness and the "shakes." Although she had nothing to drink, the husband persisted in accusing her of drinking. After about a week of total abstinence, the husband came home from work one night and said, "Honey, I'm sorry that I accused you unjustly. I think you've been a real soldier. I really believe you haven't been drinking all week. Now that you're over that horrible thing and it's all behind us, we can live normally, and we can begin going to social activities again, and you can have one or two drinks like everybody else." Whereupon he brought out a gift-wrapped bottle of scotch, with which they were going to celebrate her return to "normal, social drinking." Within two days, she was stone drunk.

What do these three cases have in common? In each case, there was a family member who was condemning the addiction and was ready to do anything and everything to bring it to an end. In each case, both the addicted person and family members were suffering as a result of the addiction. Yet in each case, the family member was doing the precise thing that would *perpetuate* the addiction rather than terminate it.

In working with alcoholism and other addictions, it becomes obvious that it is totally futile to conduct a fault-finding campaign, looking for who did what, how it all started, and who is to blame. Dwelling on these issues can result only in intense anger of everyone with everyone else and with themselves as well, and it sets up new obstacles to recovery. Furthermore, pointing the finger at alcoholics can drive them further into a corner, and since their prime method of dealing with stress is to drink rather than to fight their way out of it, they are apt to react to being cornered by increasing their drinking. On the other hand, if family members feel they are to "blame" for the person's addiction, they become defensive and critical, and they may become adversaries rather than allies in the recovery process. It is therefore imperative that we direct our attention to *what* is happening and how the factors operative in the addiction can be overcome, with no overtones of accusation or condemnation of *either* the addicted person or the family.

(One brief digresson. It is terribly disruptive to concentration, at least for me, to always include both singular pronouns, his or her, he or she, and so on. It seems that traditionally alcoholism has been considered to be primarily a male illness, but recent studies have adequately indicated that alocholism is very prevalent among females, and it is of little consequence whether the ratio of male to female alcoholism is one to one, one to three, three to one or whatever. Addiction is a serious problem in either sex. For the sake of simplicity, I will use the pronouns *he, his* in general, asking the reader to feel free to substitute *she, her.*)

Cases such as those cited and others have indicated that very frequently in instances of addiction to alcohol or other drugs, there are what can be called *enabling* factors in the addict's environment, and there are persons who, without malice, do the kinds of things that make them "enablers." In other words, some of their behavior, although well intended, enables the addiction to continue—which may be a consequence of what they are doing as well as of what they are not doing. In order to better understand what is happening, why these things may be happening, and above all how enabling factors may be avoided, it is necessary to begin with some general facts and ideas about alcoholism and other addictions.

2

Alcoholism Defined

What is alcoholism? What is addiction? Where does appropriate use of alcohol or medications stop and abuse begin? What medications are to be considered *drugs* in the addictive sense?

These are extremely important questions which are most difficult to answer with any degree of precision. To think of alcoholism in terms of a skid row derelict or of someone who has developed advanced liver disease is like thinking of cancer that has spread from its original site to many organs of the body. Just as cancer, if detected in its very early stages, can often be successfully treated, preventing the disabling and killing consequences of the widespread condition, so in alcoholism it is often possible to diagnose the condition in its early stages before the ruinous consequences of body damage, job loss, family disruption, and social and personal deterioration occur.

The analogy of alcoholism, or addiction, to cancer is consistent in many aspects. Both begin insidiously, with no symptoms whatever, so that only the most diligent and meticulous examination can reveal their presence. In both there is often an intermediate phase in which symptoms have begun to appear, but effective treatment, sometimes quite radical, can arrest the condition. In both there is a strong tendency to deny their existence and to avoid the possibility of the correct diagnosis until the condition has progressed so far that denial is no longer feasible. In both, the untreated condition progresses relentlessly toward deterioration and death; the only significant difference between the two is that the impact of alcoholism upon the family of the alcoholic, especially the spouse and the children, can be even more destructive than that of cancer. And finally, both conditions show no discrimination whatever. Rich and poor alike, male and female, black and white, young and old, bright and dull—no group is spared.

There is yet another advantage in thinking of alcoholism as analogous to cancer. There is a tendency to restrict the term *alcoholism* to the individual who has already suffered one or more of the deteriorating sequelae of alcoholism, and to refer to the less-advanced cases as *problem drinkers* or even *prealcoholics*. When cancer is discovered in the very early stages, it is not called a *premalignant* growth or any other such euphemism; it is a true cancer in the full sense of the word. The correct term indicates the most serious character of the problem and also connotes what would happen if it were neglected. The physician may refer to cancer as stage I, II, III, or IV, according to the degree of its spread, but even in stage I, it is still called by its true name. Similarly, one might talk about various stages of alcoholism, but even in the so-called "early" stages of alcoholism, it is not *prealcoholism*. It is full-fledged alcoholism, albeit in a state where disastrous consequences have not yet occurred, and there is no reason to camouflage the diagnosis. Indeed, the early alcoholic's best interest as well as that of those around him might best be served by calling the condition by its real name: *alcoholism.*

To many people in the field, particularly those who ascribe to the disease concept of alcoholism, the latter term is not repugnant. Alcoholism, like diabetes, is accepted as a disease with a wide spectrum of variants which are subtypes of the disease category.

However, centuries of viewing alcoholism as a manifestation of a degenerated personality have given a pejorative character to the term. In actual practice, semantics are of little importance. What is important is that the person affected with a destructive drinking pattern should be aware that alcohol and his psychological-physiological system are incompatible. Even Alcoholics Anonymous, which is sometimes erroneously considered dogmatic in its approach, does not require that one admit to being alcoholic. All that is necessary for membership is that one have a sincere desire to stop drinking. There is thus no need to coerce an individual into admitting he is alcoholic as an absolute prerequisite for effective treatment. Hopefully, successful treatment will result in the patient's better understanding of the nature of the condition, wherein the term *alcoholic* will then lose its negative connotation.

Among the better-known varieties of alcoholism is that of *periodic drinking.* In this instance, the individual may go for weeks or months without drinking and then has a very severe drinking episode. Sometimes he intends to go on a binge right from the outset, but frequently the drinking episode begins with the intention to have "just a few" and ends with the person drinking much more than he intended. This is a classic example of loss of control and indicates that the condition, alcoholism, already exists. Similarly, memory lapses as a result of drinking, regardless of how infrequently they occur, must be taken as symptoms of alcoholism. It is well to be aware that memory is a faculty dependent on brain function, and that any impairment of memory caused by alcohol or drug ingestion indicates that the chemical has affected the brain in some way. Although severe permanent brain damage may not as yet have occurred, the fact that the individual's brain is sensitive to the effects of alcohol should be taken as a warning that any further abuse may result in grave and permanent brain damage.

I would like to direct attention to the early stages of alcoholism because, as with cancer, successful treatment can avert tragedy. In its earliest stages, alcohol may not yet have caused *any* deleterious effects, and thus there is as yet no classic sign or symptoms. How then can such drinking be distinguished from the so-called "normal" use of alcohol?

One of the characteristics of addiction is the phenomenon of *tolerance*. Tolerance is not a personality factor nor a psychological manifestation but a very real physical-chemical phenomenon which is as immutable as the law of gravity. There may be variations in the rate of development of tolerance—that is some people may develop tolerance more rapidly, others more slowly—but it is a fairly safe generalization that tolerance itself is universal.

Tolerance is simply this. Every person's central nervous system, when continually subjected to a depressant chemical, will eventually accommodate and adapt itself in such a manner that the same amount of chemical will no longer have the same effect. This is true of the chemical alcohol (for alcohol is very much a chemical), of the barbiturates and nonbarbiturate sedatives, and of many of the tranquilizers. In other words, if a person requires a dose of a sedative drug for sleep, and he continues to use the drug regularly, it is usually only a matter of time before he finds that the drug no longer has the same effect as it did initially, and that now in order to obtain that effect, he requires a double dose of the same chemical. Eventually the body accommodates to the double dose, and a further increase is necessary to obtain the desired effect. Many people who have used alcohol with regularity have been able to consume an amount that would send a nondrinker into a stupor, but their central nervous system has so accommodated itself that they can maintain a degree of alertness even with a high blood level of alcohol. This is equally true of the other chemicals mentioned.

It should be pointed out that in many cases a reversal of tolerance eventually occurs, either because the liver becomes damaged by alcohol so that it can no longer effectively detoxify or cleanse the body of the chemical, or because progressive destruction of brain cells leaves so few functioning that depression of the remaining functioning brain tissue occurs even with small amounts of the chemical, or for other reasons yet unclear to us.

Understanding the phenomenon of tolerance enables us to accept the following definition of alcoholism, or at least of a common variety of it. *Alcoholism can be said to exist when any normal function becomes dependent on alcohol, regardless of the quantity consumed.* Eating, sleeping, socializing, sexual relations, business activity—all these are normal functions. When any one or more of them become dependent on consumption of alcohol for execution, alcoholism can be said to exist.

The question is often asked whether the person who has one or two cocktails before dinner is an alcoholic. In light of the above, the answer is that if he *cannot* eat without the drinks, then he is an alcoholic, even though he has never yet suffered a convulsion or blackout, never been arrested for drunken driving, never had a fight with his wife over alcohol, and has not sustained any apparent liver damage. The reason for this is a simple syllogism.

For example, eating is a normal function. If a person cannot eat without prior consumption of alcohol, it is because he requires a certain effect from alcohol in order to eat. We know from the phenomenon of tolerance that it is only a matter of time before he will no longer obtain that same effect from the same amount of alcohol. However, since he *requires* that effect in order to eat, it will now be necessary to increase the quantity consumed to obtain that effect; and then the cycle will repeat itself a number of times, until the signs of advanced alcoholism become grossly apparent. Since eating is a normal function with which one cannot dispense, the only possible course is the progressive increase of the amount of alcohol consumed. The same is true of every normal function of an individual's everyday life.

Case 4

A forty-two-year-old business executive came in for a consultation at the insistence of his wife, who felt he was developing a drinking problem. (Note: By the time the drinking has created an awareness of the problem by someone in the family, it is usually beyond the early stage.) The man protested that his wife was exaggerating and that much of what she said was untrue. He claimed that he had never been unruly from alcohol and had only rarely been intoxicated, but he did admit that before a business engagement, such as an executive meeting or other important transactions, he simply *had to* take one or two drinks. He insisted that he had never taken more than this, that he rarely would take more than two or three drinks daily, that this amount was causing him no harm whatever, and in fact that it enabled him to function properly. He stated that without a prior drink there was no way he could compose himself adequately to conduct the particular affairs at hand.

Based on the previous definition, I advised the man that he was indeed a confirmed alcoholic, because one of his normal functions, that of conducting business conferences and transactions, had become dependent on alcohol, and that it would only be a matter of time before affairs progressed to manifest disaster. He completely rejected this diagnosis, insisting that he had things completely under control, that he was in no way alcoholic, that he could stop drinking whenever he wished, that there was nothing harmful in his current manner of drinking, and that there was therefore no need for his becoming involved in any treatment program. Unfortunately, time proved him to be wrong, because during the next two years there was progressive increase in his drinking, leading to a great deal of family strife and culminating in his miraculously escaping serious bodily injuries in an automobile accident resulting from driving while under the influence of alcohol.

Although the accident did not shock him into recovery, it was not too long after that that he entered a treatment program. His own words in a letter are worth repeating. This letter was written several days after I met this person at a lecture I was presenting on alcoholism, which was about four years after our initial meeting.

Dear Doctor,

I was just delighted to see you again, and it was very rewarding to me to see the joy in your eyes. I'm not sure whether your initial facial expression was lack of recognition or disbelief. Whatever, it was one of those experiences where words are not needed to describe feelings; the eye communication tells it all.

I've thought quite a bit about your lecture and your closing remarks. We both know many drinkers who would pay little attention to the consequences you talked about. I believe in most people it's an illusion of immunity and not a sincere "don't care" attitude.

After the lecture, you must at times wonder "What good did it do?" In your profession, I imagine it would be easy to fall in the trap of measuring disappointments because one can't always measure the effects of his remarks on the ones who succeed.

I left there knowing I had an additional reinforcement to stay away from liquor. Periodically, I get the old desire, and what has worked thus far is to be able to weigh all the benefits of sobriety vs the pleasure (??) of drinking. I need all the reinforcement available, otherwise the denial and rationalization will surface.

Although my sobriety is only a little over six months, it has been and is a comfortable one. I'm aware that it is easy to become complacent, and for me the defense is going to a lot of meetings. Eight or nine a week is average. It is not necessarily a great need to go to so many meetings; for me it is educational, enjoyment, and the opportunity to better know the people in AA.

Since our first meeting, four years ago, my drinking has been strictly periodic. Even prior to that, I learned recently, I was a daily drinker and a periodic drunk. This makes acceptance difficult, because one hears so many in AA comment that they lost control every time they drank; how could I be one when it only happened four or five times a year? If you ever encounter a person with this pattern perhaps my story may help.

Getting back to the events after my hospitalization at ______, the pattern was erratic, but as you know, predictable. I would go for two or three months and a couple times even longer, drink for a week, two or three, then taper off and quit. After talking to you from ______hospital after the accident, I went six months—drank for two weeks, then back again—quit for a month, then back for another detox last December. Although I knew then I'd lost the battle with booze, it took three more two-week binges to get it out of my system.

During the period from December 1974, to April of this year, I went to AA meetings pretty regularly and became acquainted with ______. He arranged for me to go to______, where I spent fourteen weeks. Sometime I would like to tell you about this experience.

The firm, particulaly my supervisor, was very understanding and gave me the time with pay. For this, I'll always be grateful. My supervisor and two of my fellow workers found it difficult to believe I was alcoholic. For a long time, I thought they were being kind, but recently have found out they were really surprised to learn of my problem.

Most of my drinking in the past four years happened when on vacation, making it easier for me to hide it. In retrospect, I imagine each of them could look back and remember situations that were not quite normal.

As you can see, I've been very fortunate. However, all of the "I never" could quickly be reversed with one ounce of alcohol. I have only a couple of minor regrets for continuing to drink the past few years, because it gave me the proof needed to feel the way I now do. Fortunately the body is a great mechanism, and despite the abuse mine seems to be in pretty fair shape.

I was surprised you remembered my anxiety when speaking in front of groups. Although it is still present, there's been a marked improvement recently. Do you suppose that comes with age or could there be some other reason for the nervousness?

This was longer than I intended it to be, but writing it was good for me. Thanks for your help and interest.

Sincerely,

A widely used definition of alcoholism is that the condition exists whenever any aspect of a person's life—physical, emotional, social, or occupational—has been impaired as a result of alcohol. It is obvious that this definition links alcoholism to impairment; or in other words, signs and symptoms of deterioration have already begun to appear. From a preventive point of view, the definition we have proposed diagnoses the condition in its predestructive phase.

The question may be raised—inasmuch as it is difficult enough to get an individual to recognize his alcohol problem even when the devastating consequences of his drinking are blatant—how can one expect a person to accept a diagnosis of alcoholism when his drinking has not yet caused any apparent harm and appears to all the world like typical social "healthy" drinking? This is certainly a valid observation, yet it should not deter us from making a correct diagnosis. For example, it is now possible to diagnose pregnancy within forty-eight hours after conception, yet it is weeks before the woman has any symptoms or signs by which she can recognize her pregnancy, and it is months before the pregnancy is obvious to others. It is clear, however, that the woman is as much pregnant the moment after conception as she is in her ninth month, the only difference being the stage of pregnancy. Similarly, alcoholism exists long before the alcoholic and those about him become aware of it, but the early alcoholic is no less an alcoholic than the far-advanced case.

The difficulty in recognizing one's own alcoholism is largely a result of a process referred to as *denial*, which is one of the fundamental psychological factors in alcoholism. In order to better understand the alcoholic and, more importantly, in order to be of real help to him, we must have some understanding of denial. As we shall see, denial occurs in the environment of the addicts as well as in the addicts themselves, and for all practical purposes, recovery cannot begin until denial is first overcome.

Before going on to a discussion of denial and other psychological factors operative in the alcoholic and his environment, I would like to dwell briefly on some of the destructive consequences of alcoholism. Knowledge of the natural course of any illness is necessary if we wish to consider how much effort we are willing to put into prevention, early detection, and/or treatment.

3

Effects of Alcohol

For the reader whose interest was drawn to this book because of an alcohol problem in the family, the description of the behavioral, emotional, and psychological consequences of alcohol abuse may seem to be superfluous. Nonetheless, there is value in listing them. First, since we have tried to identify the early alcoholic—that is, the person who has developed a dependence on alcohol but has not yet reached the stage where disruption of function and family relationships has occurred—it is well for such individuals and their families to know what will eventually happen if the alcoholism is not arrested. Second, it is surprising to note that in many instances where excessive drinking has been identified as a problem, neither the drinker nor the people about him make the connection between the drinking and the behavioral troubles as cause and effect. In other words, they see that there are many things going wrong and know that there is a drinking problem, but in many instances they somehow fail to recognize that alcohol is the cause, instead attributing the negative behavior to outside circumstances or hidden psychological problems. It is therefore important to know what alcohol abuse can generate so that attention can be focused on the true cause rather than on side issues.

Alcohol is a drug that has a profound effect on the brain cells. This simple statement should suffice to raise a strong suspicion, when a person is not functioning optimally, that alcohol may be the cause. The brain has more than four and one-half billion cells, all interconnected in a complexity that would make the most complicated, sophisticated computer seem like a Tinkertoy. Intoxicating this exquisitely sensitive and complex brain with alcohol or other drugs is like hitting it with a heavy sledgehammer; in fact, that is precisely what alcohol toxicity is: a chemical sledgehammer. Obviously, a sensitive instrument struck by a sledgehammer is going to function improperly, regardless of how hard the operator of the instrument tries to make it work well.

At this point in the history of civilization, we have all become more or less aware that the human being is composed, among other things, of a bundle of impulses and emotions. Love, hate, anger, greed, envy, sexual drives, lust for power, desire for recognition, desire to be cared for—these are some of the better-known components present in all of us in a greater or lesser proportion. A well-adjusted personality, in the final analysis, is a result of a proper integration of all human emotional components, with proper control of expression of internal drives and desires. When the integrating ability is lessened or impaired, the emotional expressions are virtually bound to become chaotic. By their toxic effects on the brain, alcohol and other mind-altering chemicals seriously impair the integrating ability, with consequent disastrous emotional results.

The person under the influence of alcohol is incapable of exerting the full capacity of his judgment. Indiscretions will occur, in reckless expenditure of money, in impulsive business deals, in telling the employer to go to hell and leaving the job, in irrascible explosions at the children, in violent angry outbursts toward the wife, in physical abuse of family members, in neglect of the children, in drunken driving, in sexual indiscretions, in lying to cover up some misdeeds, in poor work performance, in disorderly conduct or other violations of the law; invariably one or more of these behavioral complications will occur. Inasmuch as the person who drinks excessively uses alcohol as a tranquilizer, it is obvious that when any of these events occurs, and he becomes depressed, tense, guilty, or remorseful because of it, he may turn once again to alcohol for relief of these very uncomfortable feelings; thus, a self-perpetuating vicious cycle is in the making. Persons familiar with alcoholic behavior know that when the alcoholic begins to feel remorseful and starts his self-flagellation, another binge is not far away.

It is clear to everyone except the alcoholic that alcohol never resolved any problem. If there is tension and pressure from a tight financial squeeze, drinking will not increase the bank account. It will only superficially blot out awareness of the problem, but the result of the drinking will be that the person is less efficient at work and less adequate in managing his financial affairs. Hence, the financial situation can only be aggravated by alcohol, and of course, as the situation deteriorates, the person is apt to drink even more.

The salient point of all this is that *unless alcoholism is arrested, the course is inexorable,* with grave behavioral and personality consequences not only for the alcoholic but also for those close to him. The impact on the emotional well-being of the spouse and children of the alcoholic is beyond estimation. Because of the nature of addiction, the alcoholic may be unable to see that the consequences of his drinking are devastatingly destructive. It is thus imperative that those in the environment of the alcoholic be fully aware of this. For all practical purposes, there is no exception. There may be a variable period of time and there may be brief intervals of apparently normal behavior, but unarrested alcoholism leads to self-destruction.

Although the behavioral consequences of alcoholism are somewhat familiar to us, relatively few people recognize the very noxious *physical* effects. There is hardly a tissue in the human body that is not damaged by alcohol abuse. Even those who are under the false impression that the alcoholic has full control of his behavior should realize that once alcohol enters the body, *no one* has any control over what it does. Alcohol is a chemical, and chemical reactions follow their own rules.

Alcohol has a very irritating effect on the gastric mucosa, or the lining of the stomach. Continued exposure to alcohol, or exposure to large amounts of alcohol, results in alcoholic gastritis, with pain, nausea, and vomiting—symptoms quite familiar to the alcoholic. Serious hemorrhage, with vomiting of blood, can occur, as can acute gastric dilatation, resulting even in death. Furthermore, the acid output of the stomach is greatly increased by alcohol intake, so that the lining of the stomach and the first part of the small intestine are exposed to an acid-alcohol mixture, frequently resulting in peptic ulcers of the stomach or duodenum, with possible perforation or hemorrhage.

The liver is very sensitive to the toxic effects of alcohol. Cirrhosis, which is the last stage of alcoholic liver disease, is one of the five leading causes of death in this country at present. The liver is the body's "chemical plant," and impairment of liver function can cause severe and widespread harm. Among the consequences of this impairment, which can be extremely and suddenly disastrous, is that related to blood coagulation, or clotting.

It is well known that some people are hemophilic;

that is, their blood cannot coagulate rapidly or even at all. In healthy people, damage to a broken blood vessel is quickly repaired by the body's wonderful built-in "repair kit," which consists of a number of chemicals that have a gluelike action. If a blood vessel is opened by a cut or bruise, these chemicals immediately form a plug that seals off the damaged blood vessels, thus stopping the bleeding. Hemophilia is caused by an absence of one or more of the substances necessary to form a clot, and thus even a very minor injury can cause serious or even fatal hemorrhage.

The substances responsible for blood coagulation are manufactured in the liver, and when the liver function is impaired by alcohol, even long before the liver is anywhere near the stage of cirrhosis, there can be a very serious deficiency in the production of the blood-clotting substances; the person may then be a "bleeder." This is why so many alcoholics have a tendency toward easy bruising, discovering large black and blue marks over their skin, even in the absence of any falls or blows. Although these skin bruises may be of only cosmetic significance, more serious internal bleeding can occur.

Case 5

Evaline is a forty-nine-year-old married woman, who had a drinking problem for many years but resisted any treatment. One day her husband called, stating that Evaline was now willing to enter a rehabilitation center. He then added that he was calling from Evaline's room in a hospital and that she had undergone brain surgery several days earlier.

On visiting Evaline, I learned that about ten days previously her husband had noted that she was very drowsy, but concluded that she just must have been drinking more than usual. Her drowsiness kept on increasing, and one day he was unable to arouse her at all. She was taken to the hospital, where tests revealed a blood clot on the surface of the brain, and she underwent surgery to remove the clot.

What had happened to Evaline was that she had fallen at home and had bumped her head. She thought nothing of the fall and got up and walked away. However, the blow to her head had caused a tiny blood vessel on the surface of the brain to crack open; since her blood-clotting mechanism was defective because of the liver damage caused by the alcohol, the blood vessel did not seal. For the next few days, she kept slowly oozing blood inside her skull, eventually resulting in coma.

Unfortunately, removal of the clot by surgery did not prevent some permanent brain damage, and Evaline was never the same again mentally. This is an example of how an otherwise insignificant fall was converted into a major disaster because of liver damage resulting from alcohol abuse.

The liver also functions as the body's "manufacturing plant," and it receives most of its raw materials from the intestines, where the food is digested, dissolved, and absorbed by the blood vessels, which carry the products of digestion to the liver. All the blood vessels from the abdominal organs join together to form the portal vein, a very large blood vessel which carries enormous quantities of blood to the liver. This blood rapidly traverses the liver and is returned to the general circulation. The blood is able to pass through the liver rapidly because there are thousands of blood channels there that can accommodate this massive blood flow.

When liver tissue is damaged by alcohol, it eventually heals, and the healed tissue forms a scar. After a period of time, these scars contract (just as do scars in skin tissue), and the blood vessels are trapped among the scars and are pinched off. Repeated drinking results in much scar formation, and eventually enough blood channels are pinched off so that blood flow through the liver is impeded. The situation is analogous to a six-lane freeway, where several of the lanes have been obstructed by car wrecks, resulting in congestion and backup of traffic; oncoming cars are forced to seek an alternate route around the obstructed area.

When cirrhosis, or scarring, of the liver obstructs the normal blood flow, the blood must find alternate ways of getting back into circulation. One of the detours is through small blood vessels at the juncture of the esophagus and the stomach. Because these vessels are forced to stretch to accommodate the large amount of blood being channeled through them, the dilated veins become varicose veins, quite similar to varicose veins on the legs. However, these thin-walled veins are prone to rupture, and being in an inaccessible place, rupture results in serious and often fatal hemorrhage.

Case 6

Katherine was a fifty-three-year-old woman who drank excessively. She felt that she was not an alcoholic because she only drank beer, and she hid her drinking by drinking only at home and usually when her husband and children were away. No amount of coaxing could get Katherine to seek help for her drinking problem, primarily because she did not feel that she had a problem.

One afternoon, Katherine's husband returned home from work to find her on the floor in a stupor. She was taken to a hospital, where she died without ever becoming conscious. An autopsy revealed that she had died of an internal hemorrhage from a ruptured varicose vein in the esophagus.

The important feature of this case is that Katherine had never previously shown any signs of liver disease. The first indication of her problem was also the last.

In addition to the complications of hemorrhage from ruptured esophageal veins or blood-clotting deficiency, many other serious consequences can result from liver disease, among them jaundice, edema, accumulation of toxic materials in the blood, and metabolic disturbances.

As was mentioned earlier, alcohol and drugs have a depressant effect on the brain cells; in fact, this numbing effect is precisely why the chemical is used, since this is how it provides its tranquilizing effect. Prolonged or excessive use of these substances, however, can cause irreversible or permanent depression of brain tissue, resulting in untreatable brain damage.

Case 7

Marilyn was an attractive thirty-nine-year-old woman when she was admitted to the hospital for the fourth time for "drying out." Her marriage had been terminated because of her drinking, and her children would have nothing to do with her. She had completely alienated her parents with her drunken behavior, and when the parents were called by the hospital social worker to help plan Marilyn's recovery, they simply hung up the phone.

Marilyn reluctantly consented to enter a rehabilitation program but never took it seriously. On discharge she rejected outpatient follow-up or involvement with AA.

Three years later, I received a request for a consultation on the medical ward and recognized Marilyn's name. On the ward, I passed her by without recognizing her, and when the nurse pointed her out to me, it was difficult to believe that this tragic, haggard shell that was sitting with a sheet around her waist holding her down to the chair was the bright and lively woman of only three years ago.

The sheet restraint was necessary because Marilyn's legs could not support her. The erosion of her nerve tissue by alcohol had made her legs functionless; she had no concept of time, did not know whether it was summer or winter, and had bizarre delusions. After six weeks of intensive vitamin therapy, her legs regained some function, but her brain never recovered. There was no alternative other than to commit her to a state hospital, where her mental state has remained unchanged even after a year. It is evident that Marilyn will live out the remaining years of her life in a state institution.

The gravity of brain damage cannot be overemphasized. No medication, surgery, nor any type of psychiatric treatment can restore brain cells that have been killed by alcohol or drugs. When alcohol begins to cause temporary memory lapses, or blackouts, or when it causes a convulsion or hallucinations, this should serve as a warning signal that alcohol is getting to the brain and that serious trouble may be ahead.

Severe anemias are common in alcoholism, in spite

of adequate diet and even high vitamin intake. Blood-sugar levels can be raised by alcohol, giving a diabetic-like picture, and persons with a tendency toward diabetes can become frankly diabetic because of the effect of alcohol on the liver and pancreas. Hypoglycemia, or low blood sugar, can also be caused by the liver damage. Lung diseases of various kinds are more common and more serious in alcoholics, not only because of their lower body resistance and ineffective body response to infection, but also because the protective reflexes that help keep foreign material out of the lungs are rendered inactive by alcohol. Alcohol aggravates high blood pressure and also has a direct injurious effect on heart muscle. Severe deterioration of all nerve elements of the body can result from excessive alcohol.

From both physical and behavioral aspects, there should be no question in anyone's mind that alcoholism is relentlessly destructive. Yet in spite of apparent awareness of this fact, the alcoholic returns to drinking even after suffering serious physical consequences.

Case 8

> A company physician was advised by his employer that he could either get help with his drinking problem or he would lose his job. On entering the hospital, he stated that his longest recent period of sobriety had been six weeks. His vision had become blurred, and after examination by an eye specialist, he was told that he had an inflammation of the optic nerve because of alcohol and that he might lose his vision. After six weeks of complete abstinence, his vision improved, whereupon he went right back to drinking.

The psychological quirk responsible for the alcoholic's inability to recognize his problem is what we previously referred to as denial. We can now examine this phenomenon and see in what way enablers sometimes aid and abet its operation.

4

Dealing with Denial

Just what is meant by the term *denial*? Obviously, it indicates that someone is denying something, and in our context, it refers to the person's denying the fact that he has an alcohol problem. The concept can easily be misunderstood, however, since one can think of denial as the alcoholic's classic proclivity to lying—which is present in great abundance. One alcoholic with many years of sobriety once advised me, "You can always tell when an 'alky' is lying by watching his lips. If they're moving, he's lying." This is a fairly safe rule of thumb applied to the active drinker, especially in relation to the amount or pattern of his drinking. But the term *denial* as used in relationship to the alcoholic is something quite different. Lying is a conscious process; the person knows he is lying. Denial is generally unconscious; that is, the person is unaware that he is doing it. Denial is one of the defense mechanisms referred to in psychology as one of a person's *unconscious* mechanisms. It is present in many emotional disorders, but hardly anywhere as obviously as in the alcoholic.

In order to clarify what is meant by denial, I would like to present an example from another illness. During my year of internship, I met a patient, a woman of forty-four, who had undergone surgery for cancer. Before her operation, she told the doctor that she was very active in many civic projects and was carrying major responsibilities. She stated that because of these, it was absolutely necessary that she know the truth about her condition and that she couldn't afford the luxury of being falsely reassured or comforted; unless she took the proper steps to transfer her responsibilities, many vital projects would suffer if she were to become incapacitated. The doctor respected her wishes, and when it was discovered that she indeed had cancer, he told her the true diagnosis, advising her that there was reason for believing that the condition could be controlled by medication. The patient thanked him and said that she would cooperate fully in any prescribed treatment.

The patient received an anticancer drug that had to be given intravenously; unfortunately, her veins were difficult to find, so that each injection was an ordeal of multiple punctures. One time I administered the medication and was lucky to succeed on the first try. She thereafter insisted that I was the only one who could give her the injections, and this became a weekly routine. For almost a full year, she came in regularly every week, asking for her "cancer shot," speaking freely about having cancer and how fortunate she was to benefit from the new discoveries of medication. We were all quite impressed with the courage and maturity of this woman and her acceptance of her condition.

After about a year, she began complaining of various symptoms, and it was suspected that the cancer was no longer inhibited by the medication. Unfortunately, there was nothing more that could be done for her. Gradually her symptoms became worse, with weakness, multiple pains, and marked shortness of breath, necessitating her hospitalization. On her admission to the hospital, I did the routine workup, and was completely taken aback when she said, "I don't understand what's wrong with you doctors. I've been coming here for over a year, and you can't seem to find out what the trouble is with me."

This is an example of what is meant by the psychological term *denial*. When recognition of something is too devastating, there can occur an automatic shutoff of that recognition. It is somewhat akin to the phenomenon of fainting because of intolerable pain, which is nature's method of providing relief through a state of unawareness. It is important to realize that just as one does not consciously and willfully determine to faint, so one does not consciously and willfully bring about denial.

In the case cited, the woman was able to accept the fact that she had cancer as long as it was not something that was very real to her, as long as it was only a scientific term, and as long as she only had to think about it in the abstract. When the condition made itself felt in a very real fashion, her system turned off her entire awareness of it.

Much the same happens with the alcoholic. Initially, he totally denies that he drinks too much or that any of his problems are related to his drinking, although it is so obvious to everyone else. At a later stage, he may give lip service to admitting alcoholism, as much as to say, "All right, you say I am an alcoholic, so I admit I am an alcoholic. Now get off my back and leave me alone." Down deep, however, at the gut level, he still denies his alcoholism and so does not do anything serious to overcome it. Inasmuch as sincere efforts at recovery cannot occur until denial is overcome, it is of overriding importance to see in what ways this can be accomplished.

Although the following story seems amusing, it is actually quite instructive, since it points out how far the denial of alcoholism can go.

Case 9

A young business executive, who had risen very rapidly in the corporate structure because of his unusual abilities, began drinking heavily and regularly. His friends at the company as well as his family pleaded with him to cut back on his drinking, but he refused to listen. He insisted that he could not be alcoholic because he never drank the "hard stuff," only beer. Eventually his work began to deteriorate, and after numerous warnings from his superiors, he was demoted. He was told point blank that the demotion was the result of alcohol impairing his work; but he refused to recognize it, concluding instead that others were envious of him because of his rise to a higher echelon at so young an age and were "out to get him."

Eventually, he began to have various physical symptoms, and although a physician made it clear to him that these were the effects of alcohol, he dismissed this also, concluding instead that he was simply taking too many "fluids"; he thereupon switched from beer to whiskey and soda. His physical symptoms continued to progress, and he then decided that carbonated water was the culprit, switching to whiskey and water. His demotions at work continued, but this had no impact whatever since he was still convinced that he was a victim of others' envy. Further worsening of his physical symptoms then brought a conclusion that he was still taking too many "fluids," and he eliminated the water, continuing on straight whiskey. He was eventually demoted to a custodial position and, finally, was unable to keep even this job. After being fired, he would sit in beer gardens and drink, fantasizing that some major corporation president would come in and offer him a job as executive vice-president.

There is an axiom among recovered alcoholics that "no alcoholic recovers until he hits rock bottom." This truism is a realization emanating from decades of experience with thousands of cases. It is simply a restatement in very figurative language of the earlier observation that recovery does not occur until there is a breakthrough in the defense of denial. Persons involved in helping alcoholics have long recognized that all efforts—lecturing, threatening, cajoling, pleading, frightening, bribing, and countless others—are futile until something occurs that breaks through the denial and brings about the gut-level awareness that one is indeed an alcoholic, that one is indeed an addict. This "something" is the rock bottom that must be reached.

Rock bottom is highly variable. There are "high" rock-bottom persons, and there are those with "low" rock bottoms. There are those who appear to be "bottomless"; that is, they die before reaching their bottom, or to put it another way, their rock bottom is death. Just as tragic, or even more so, is the person who hits rock bottom in such a state of deterioration that he is much like Humpty Dumpty: too shattered to be put back together again.

Bottoming-out is a highly individual happening. One young man, now in his second year of sobriety, continued drinking after his wife and children left him, after his wife divorced him, after his parents rejected him, after he was arrested for disorderly conduct, after he was hospitalized with a severe stomach hemorrhage. Throughout he managed to hold onto his job, but when his supervisor called him in and told him he was going to be fired because his drinking had made his job performance unacceptable, he came asking for help and has since made a successful recovery. It is incorrect to conclude that he loved his job more than his family. Perhaps with this man, as with many others, bottoming-out was a combined result of a number of contributing factors, and the ego-shattering threat of job loss may have been the proverbial straw that broke the camel's back.

The following two examples indicate the variability in rock bottom:

Case 10

> A thirty-nine-year-old housewife was brought by her husband for evaluation of her alcohol problem. There had been years of family strife and bickering because of her drinking, and her children had expressed their bitter disappointment to her. As her husband recounted the family disruption that her drinking had caused, she admitted all the incidents; yet she continued to deny that she needed help, stating that she could stop whenever she pleased. She refused any treatment at this time.
>
> Several months later, she was again seen, this time at her own request. The drinking had continued, and in a fit of rage during a family squabble, she had picked up the color television set and smashed it in the presence of the children. On one occasion, she had rendered her husband unconscious by hitting him over the head with a skillet. At this point, the recommendation was for her to enter an inpatient rehabilitation program, and although she was willing to accept that she might need some help with

her drinking, she rejected this particular recommendation.

After several months, the woman requested admission to the rehabilitation center. Upon admission, she stated that several days earlier she had awaked on the floor and could not remember how she had gotten there. She had obviously suffered a convulsion, and for this woman this was finally the rock bottom that brought her into treatment.

Case 11

A thirty-seven-year-old man came to the office completely on his own, requesting help with a drinking problem. He stated that his pattern of drinking had been on evenings and weekends only and that he had never had any job interference at all. The quantity of alcohol consumed had increased some over the years, but he had never been abusive at home. However, his wife had been extremely critical of his drinking and had pleaded with him many times to stop. One week earlier, the wife had taken her pillow and moved out to the couch. She advised him that for the children's sake she was going to keep the family unit together, but they were not going to live as husband and wife. It was at this time that he determined he would request help.

On the following day, he advised his partner in his office that he was going to get some help with his alcohol problem. The partner was astonished, saying that he had not had any inkling that the man drank to excess.

In this case, although the drinking had not been behaviorally disruptive outside the family and by many standards would be considered problem drinking in a very early phase, the rejection by the wife constituted a rock bottom.

A great deal may be going on in the environment of the alcoholic, which may prevent a breakthrough in the denial, thus lowering the rock bottom. We have seen that although alcohol is clearly harming the drinker, he tries in various ways to cover up its deleterious effects, sometimes attributing the harm to other causes, and at other times, actually deluding himself that no harm is occurring. If those in the environment of the alcoholic help cover up the harm that is being done or attribute it to other causes, they are actually promoting the progression of the condition and permitting the denial to persist, and the addiction to progress.

5

Fantasy of Omnipotence

You will recall that in Case 1, the wife complained that the husband was totally destroying himself. It was pointed out to her that by supporting him, she was actually enabling him to continue his destructive drinking. Yet she could not cut off her support of his addiction because of "what it might do to him." This seems confusing and contradictory. If she really believed that he was indeed destroying himself, and she could understand that her support was perpetuating the drinking, why should she believe that discontinuing this support would be harmful to him? The answer can only be that just as the husband had a denial of his own regarding his drinking, so had the wife. She was saying the right words, but she never really accepted them deep down at the gut level. Neither of the two had the insight that would enable them to get out of the rut that they were in.

Why should someone not be able to see something that is right before his very eyes? Probably because such perception would be so devastating to the personality that it is blotted out, a kind of psychological blind spot.

As was pointed out earlier in the case of the woman who accepted her cancer until she actually found it life-threatening, there is an automatic safety valve within us that can turn off our perception of something that would be devastating to our personality.

One of the things that seems to be going on within the alcoholic is a fantasy of power and control. He sees himself as all-powerful in relation to alcohol, when the truth is just the reverse; he is power*less* over alcohol; it is all-powerful over him. In psychological terms this is referred to as a *fantasy of omnipotence*, and it is encountered in virtually every active alcoholic. The phrases, "I can stop any time I wish" or "I can take it or leave it alone," are expressions of the alcoholic's sense of power and control; although it is perfectly obvious that he is totally unable to stop and can never leave it alone.

Many alcoholics go through periods of several weeks of abstinence; they proudly boast that they have liquor all around them in the house and it does not bother them, or that they walk into a bar and drink ginger ale while everyone else is drinking beer and whiskey. When an alcoholic tells me this about himself I know that he has gotten nowhere yet in his recovery. He is still entangled in that omnipotent fantasy, which is apt to lead him next to pour a drink and sit and stare at it for two consecutive hours in order to demonstrate how powerful he really is. Not too long afterward, this bizarre idea of control will result in his concluding that anyone who had the ability to sit and look at a drink for two hours without touching it can certainly stop after one drink if he wishes. Then he takes his first drink, and he's off to the races again.

Case 12

A young housewife, a mother of two, who was on the verge of having her children taken from her because of her alcoholism, went through a rehabilitation program with what she felt was flying colors. She was absolutely certain that she was never going to drink again and that she had the whole thing conquered. She did not feel that she needed any involvement with Alcoholics Anonymous, because she had gotten it all together herself. She simply was never going to drink again.

Within one week after she left the rehabilitation center, I learned that she had visited a liquor store. On questioning her, she admitted that she had indeed bought liquor, but triumphantly declared that she had not touched one single drop of it. Why then had she bought it? To prove to herself that she could have it in the house and not drink it.

The persistence of the omnipotent fantasy indicated that she really had not come to grips at all with her problem. Indeed, one week afterward she was again drinking heavily.

It is apparent that this sense of control or power in regard to alcohol is of immense importance to the alcoholic, but the reasons for it are not completely clear. The same person, if he found that he had a severe allergic reaction to chocolate or tomatoes, would have no difficulty, even when served in public, to declare openly that he is allergic to them. However, he cannot admit to himself or to anyone else that he has a kind of sensitivity to alcohol, for which reason he must avoid it. Perhaps there is a kind of cultural feeling that to have mastery over alcohol is an indication of one's strength of character; hence the boast, "I can drink anyone under the table." It is as though the inability to control alcohol is an intolerable admission of a weakness, totally different from the inability to handle chocolate or tomatoes. But whereas this explanation sounds quite logical and may be true, it is by itself inadequate to explain the universality of this phenomenon and its intensity in all alcoholics.

Case 13

A thirty-five-year-old man was admitted to the hospital because of alcoholism. On the first interview, he appeared very shaky. He felt it was a mistake to be on the alcoholic ward, because even though he drank "occasionally," he was certainly not an alcoholic. He said that his parents, who had brought him to the hospital, were making a mountain out of a molehill.

Later that day, the nurse reported that he appeared confused and was looking for his parents under the beds. Within a few hours, he began having frightening visual hallucinations, and he tried to jump out of a window to escape the men who were chasing him with axes and spears. His heart rate increased to 200 beats per minute, and it was necessary to transfer him to the intensive care unit to prevent his dying from heart failure. (Incidentally, his mother later reported that she had found more than 100 empty whiskey bottles in his room.)

In spite of all treatment, his heart rate continued exceedingly rapid for four days, during which he hardly slept at all and had to be restrained. He was constantly hallucinating and crying, alternating between cursing at his hallucinated persecutors and begging mercy from them not to kill him. The persistence of his rapid heart rate was life-threatening, and the patient was given the last rites of the Church. On the fifth day, he went into a deep sleep, and during the twenty-hour sleep, his heart rhythm finally slowed down.

Upon awakening from the long sleep, he appeared much improved and his hallucinations were gone. He had little recall of what had happened during the past few days. It was explained to him why he was in the intensive care unit, how close he had been to death, and that he had been given the last rites. He was given to understand that his recovery was virtually a resurrection. On the following day, he was moved out of the intensive care unit, but because of the recent problem with his heart, he was not returned to the alcoholic unit and instead was given a room not far from intensive care. He stated that his close call with death had finally made him realize how dangerous alcohol was to him and that he was through with it forever.

Two days later, the nurse remarked to me that the patient was requesting unusual amounts of mouthwash, and I quickly gathered that he was now drinking the mouthwash, which contains about 15 percent alcohol. When I confronted him, he vehemently denied it, but I advised him that a simple blood test could reveal whether he had any alcohol in his system or not. He then admitted that he had indeed been drinking the mouthwash. His explanation: "There's no way I could get drunk on that stuff. Too much of it will make you sick to the stomach." Only forty-eight hours after being close to death from alcohol, he was back drinking, this time believing that he had found a new way to control the amount he consumed, by drinking something that would make him sick before he got to the drunken stage.

Does this type of thinking appear to be insane? Try relating this story to a recovered alcoholic, and he will easily understand the bizarre logic that this patient employed. Thus, there is some truth to the frequently heard statement that "only an alcoholic can understand another alcoholic."

I believe it is now apparent why the first step in recovery is for the alcoholic to recognize and sincerely accept the fact, "I am powerless over alcohol." We refer to this as the process of surrender, and what it amounts to is overcoming the denial and accepting one's lack of control over alcohol.

Just as the active alcoholic persists in erroneously believing that he has control over alcohol, so those in the environment of the alcoholic have an equally erroneous belief that they can control the alocholic. They adhere to this belief tenaciously, with the same fervor and with the same degree of defiance of reality as does the alcoholic. The various techniques, methods, or tricks whereby they try to accomplish this control are no less amazing than those the alcoholic uses to try to control his drinking. Both are total failures, and this brings us to the important realization. *The alcoholic has no control over alcohol; those around the alcoholic have no control over the alcoholic.*

Rules of thumb must be approached with caution because there are sometimes exceptions. However, we can suggest two rules of thumb as guidelines for the family of the alcoholic: (1) Do not cater to alcoholic behavior, and (2) do not do as the alcoholic does. Both of these points require clarification.

It is surprising to see how often the family of the alcoholic will give in to his "crazy" behavior. He may come home from work very late, perhaps four hours after dinner time, having spent the interval in a pub, and his wife will be waiting for him, keeping his supper warm in the oven. He raises a ruckus about some trivial act of the children, and the wife shoos the kids upstairs to keep peace in the house. He has a hangover and cannot get to work, and his wife follows his instructions to call in at work and lie for him. He is too drunk to drive to the office, and she drives him. He lies on the sofa all day and drinks, and the wife works to support him. He is too unsteady to go out of the house, and the wife obediently goes to the liquor store for him. He breaks up his social life, alienating his friends, in-laws, and even his own family, and the wife meekly resigns herself to a life of loneliness. These kinds of accommodations also can be found with the alcoholic wife. In the case of an alcoholic son or daughter, catering to the alcoholism can be even more intense. Parents will see their child literally turn the house into a shambles without taking any action. They will continue to give the child money for his destructive habit. If he steals things from them, they will not press charges; if he passes worthless checks or is arrested for drunken driving, they will help him with the law.

I am not saying that the alcoholic is manipulating things by design or plan; he is often too drunk or too mixed up to design or plan anything. The point is that if drinking leads to uncomfortable consequences, and if he is permitted to evade these uncomfortable consequences, then he will simply continue headstrong into his addiction, with everything going from bad to worse. In short, addiction should not be rewarded.

I can hear the wife say, "If I refuse to call my husband's employer and cover up for him, he will lose his job, and then where will we all be? Why should I penalize myself and the children?" This is a logical question, but it betrays an unawareness of the nature of alcohol addiction. Wives who have helped their husbands hold onto their jobs will tell you that they achieved only a very temporary financial security. Eventually the husband's drinking reached a point where the poor performance and absenteeism resulted in dismissal. However, instead of coming to terms with his alcoholism at age thirty-two, when something could have been worked out with the employer and the job held for him while he obtained treatment, the addiction was permitted to progress until he was fired at age forty-five, with severe physical problems resulting from the prolonged drinking, at an age when it was much more difficult to be hired (particularly with a record of being dismissed because of drinking), and at a time when the children's education was now jeopardized because of the loss of regular income. It is a serious mistake to believe that one can prevent the loss of a job by covering up alcoholism. At best, it can be delayed, but the delay is in the long run disastrous for both the alcoholic and his family.

The alcoholic, of course, deludes himself into thinking he can maintain his job indefinitely—which is part and parcel of the denial and the fantasy of omnipotence described earlier. It is unfortunate that the family is pulled into this delusion, understandably trying to protect its security but ironically accomplishing just the reverse. On the other hand, when prompt and decisive action is taken, appropriate treatment can save a young person's life and career.

Case 14

John is a thirty-three-year-old insurance underwriter who came to the rehabilitation center accompanied by his wife for help with his drinking problem. He had just recently moved into the city and taken a job, but he was drinking heavily and regularly and recognized that his drinking was incompatible with job performance. I asked him whether his last job was terminated because of drinking, but he denied this. At this point, the wife said, "John, you're here for help. Why don't you tell the doctor the truth?" He then admitted that he had been asked to resign or he would be fired because of drinking.

I advised John that he had come to the right place and that we could begin his course in recovery with detoxification and a four-week stay in the rehabilitation center. "No way," John said. "You don't expect me to come to my boss after being on the job for only six weeks and ask for a four-week leave for treatment, do you? It will cost me my job." I told John that if he did not come in for treatment it would definitely result in the loss of his job, but that if he did come in, there was at least a possibility that his employer might consider retaining him. John rejected the recommendation, insisting that he was going to do it his way.

About three weeks later, John called to tell me that he had not taken a drink since he had seen me and that he was feeling great. I urged him to get involved with the Alcoholics Anonymous program and not to try to go it alone.

Several months later, I came to the rehabilitation center and found that John had been admitted there a day earlier. He told me that about a week after his last conversation with me, he had decided that since he had completely abstained for one month, he was now able to control his drinking, he began to drink moderately, but it soon got out of hand. I inquired about his job, and he said that he had been fired because of his drinking.

In this case, as in all others, it was the drinking that cost him his job, not his attempt at recovery. Had he taken the four weeks off initially, even if the employer would have fired him then, it would not have hurt his job prospects as much as did his being fired because of drinking.

Case 15

Robert was thirty-seven when he was admitted to the hospital for detoxification. He had been hospitalized elsewhere on four other occasions and had already had several convulsions because of his drinking. He was an engineer and held an important executive position in a large firm.

After being dried out, Robert remained sober for four weeks; he then went to Washington on a business trip, from which he returned drunk. He was again hospitalized for drying out, and the next I heard about him was some six weeks later when his wife called from their vacation site several hundred miles away. She said Robert was drunk again, and I advised her to come home and bring him to the hospital.

Several days later, the wife called to say that they were back in town, but that her husband refused to come to the hospital. I suggested to her that she immediately begin commitment procedures. She responded, "Me commit Bob? Never! He'd hold it against me for the rest of my life."

I explained to the wife that Bob had already had several convulsions, indicating that alcohol was affecting his brain, and that there was no predictability concerning which drink might bring about irreversible brain damage. I told her that inasmuch as Bob's livelihood was dependent on his being able to retain and process a great deal of detailed information, he would be rendered completely ineffective by even minimal brain damage and that his entire career could be ruined. The wife then recognized that permitting the drinking to continue would be destructive to Bob, and she agreed to institute commitment. Very soon afterward, Bob realized the futility of his resistance and came to the hospital voluntarily, initiating a gratifying recovery which is now in its ninth year. Bob has since had significant promotions.

In this case, it was the wife's determination to commit him that saved Bob's brain, career, and probably his very life. Reluctance on her part might have appeared to be "considerate" but would have allowed his addiction to destroy him.

Having mentioned commitment, it is well to say a few words about it. Involuntary commitment should be considered only on the recommendation of some expert in alcoholism. It can easily be misused by the family as another futile technique to attempt to control the alcoholic. I have seen patients released from a year's commitment to a state hospital who stopped off at the first bar they could reach, to compensate for a year's deprivation. In the case cited, I recommended commitment because I felt that the patient was at a point where the next binge could result in irreversible brain damage. There may be other considerations that could warrant commitment, but these must be weighed carefully and the decision reached with the help of an objective, unbiased person who is knowledgeable in the treatment of alcoholism.

Will the alcoholic resent commitment? Of course he will, just as an infant will resist an injection that will immunize him against diphtheria and lockjaw. All the infant can see and feel is a sharp, painful needle, and he has no way of understanding that this momentary painful procedure will save his life and prevent dreaded suffering. In absence of such realization, he will struggle and kick at his mother and the doctor. So with the alcoholic, who in his addiction cannot grasp that what is being done for him is life-saving and not punitive.

The analogy is a good one, because a commitment should never be utilized without the same sincere love and consideration that a mother has for her child. It should never be used as a threat, and it should never be used punitively. There are foolish mothers who will attempt to discipline an unruly child by saying, "If you don't behave I'll call the doctor, and he'll give you a shot," thus converting the physician from a helper to an archenemy. However, no adult resents having been immunized as an infant; instead he clearly appreciates having been forcibly given the life-saving vaccine at a time when he could not possibly have willingly accepted it.

Case 16

Ted was fifty-two when he was brought to the hospital after having suffered a convulsion from alcohol. He had a long history of excessive drinking, and his liver tests revealed extensive damage. His drinking had resulted in separation from his wife and children. He had built up a lucrative business, which was now suffering from his alcoholic behavior.

During the next two years, Ted had several hospitalizations for drying out, with intervals of several months of sobriety. During these relapses, he would fire all the employees in his business, and it was only because of the dedicated help of one of his managers that the business was not totally ruined.

On the occasion of a particular relapse, I called his estranged wife and requested that she initiate a commitment procedure, since I felt that Ted was in imminent danger of brain damage. The wife stated that although she was still legally his spouse, there was no emotional involvement between them and that she did not feel it was her place to commit him. Other family members refused to become involved, since he was still legally married to his wife.

Ted sobered up again, but several months later I heard that he had resumed his drinking. I telephoned him, and his speech indicated that he was under the influence of alcohol. I told him that I had called to say goodbye; when he asked where I was going, I told him that I was not going anywhere, but inasmuch as I was aware of his precarious liver and brain condition, and since he had resumed drinking, I expected that he would be going away for a long, long trip. I said I called to say goodbye and to let him know that I was sincerely sorry this had happened, that I wanted him to know that I thought he was really a nice guy after all.

Ted began crying and then asked if my call had anything to do with the fact that his estranged wife had returned to town that day. I told him that I had no knowledge of where his wife was, and that in fact I was quite disappointed with her for refusing to follow my recommendations for commitment.

Ted became furious. "That g--d--- b----. She could yell and nag at me, but when told what to do to save my life, she refuses!"

I believe that had the wife gone ahead with the commitment, Ted would probably have vigorously resisted. However, his comment certainly indicates that his resentment would not have been wholehearted. In fact, his resentment over not being coerced into help, which indicated that she did not care enough about his life to try and save him, was undoubtedly much greater than that of a commitment would have been.

The laws regarding commitment of an alcoholic vary from state to state, and competent legal advice, in consultation with an expert in alcoholism, must be obtained if involuntary treatment is being considered.

6

The Folly of Concealment

A frequent delusion of the alcoholic is the belief that others are not aware of his excessive drinking. Often this delusion is presented as an argument against treatment. The alocholic states that he cannot be treated nor go to AA lest it lead to the discovery by others that he had a drinking problem. Almost invariably, the alcoholic is actually the last to discover his problem. His family, friends, peers, and even employer have usually recognized it before he did.

A prominent professional person related his reluctance to join AA because of fear of exposing his condition. In retrospect, he recognized that one only had to walk past his office building when he emerged in order to make this startling discovery. Once, he recalls, a client presented him with a turkey shortly before Christmas. He left the office that rainy day carrying the turkey wrapped in butcher paper; he next recalls coming to his senses several hours later, leaning against the building with a greasy turkey under his arm, the paper having been washed away by the rain. This tragic-comic spectacle was there for all passersby to observe, yet he avoided a church where an AA meeting was held lest it lead to his exposure!

Although delusions are apt to persist in spite of factual evidence to the contrary, it certainly is of no help to support a delusion. If we know that someone for whom we care has a drinking problem, keeping our awareness a secret is detrimental. We should be able to tell a friend, a relative, or co-worker that we have noticed either excessive drinking or deleterious effects of alcohol.

It is not unusual for some women to keep their pregnancy a secret in the early months, yet the condition will reach a stage where concealment is no longer possible. Much the same can be said for pathologic drinking, with the significant difference being that concealment of pregnancy is of no harm, whereas hiding the evidence of a drinking problem may delay effective treatment.

Case 17

Charlotte is a young woman who had been most reluctant to acknowledge her drinking problem. For years she had tried to get help from psychiatrists for "anxiety and depression," until finally her excessive drinking became apparent to both her husband and herself. At this time I recommended a four-week inpatient rehabilitation program.

Charlotte stated that there was no way she could take four weeks off from work for this purpose. She knew her company's attitude toward alcoholism. A four-week absence would undoubtedly lead to suspicion of her problem and would certainly result in her dismissal.

Several months later Charlotte called, quite panicky. A group of employees of her firm, including some executives, had made a plane trip together. On the plane she took a Bloody Mary, and that is the last thing she recalls of the flight. She was subsequently advised that she had become drunk and that her behavior had been repugnant. She was now afraid to go back to the office.

I advised Charlotte that the only course open to her was to confirm for her employers what they already knew, namely, that she was an alcoholic, and to tell them that now she was going to involve herself in treatment. She later reported that she had done so and that her fantasied termination had not materialized.

As with any progressive illness, the earlier the condition is identified, the greater the likelihood of effective treatment with the least complications. Permitting alcohol abuse to continue by covering up for the drinker or allowing him to believe that his drinking problem is a well-kept secret permits progression to stages where serious and even irreversible damage may occur.

7

Role of the Self-Concept in Alcoholism

Alcoholism is a complex condition, involving many personality traits in the drinker and in the significant others in his environment. One of the important factors operative in all concerned is the self-concept.

The role of the self-image in many personality difficulties has been dealt with extensively in another work.* Here I wish to focus on its relevance in alcoholism.

Many people are victims of a negative self-image. That is to say, they have unwarranted and unjustified feelings of inadequacy. Whereas objectively and factually they may have many personality assets, they may consider themselves less attractive, less bright, less personable, or less competent than they are in reality. Not infrequently a paradox can be noted, wherein people who are particularly well endowed with fine personalities have intense feelings of inadequacy—in gross contradiction to the facts as everyone else sees them. This is most

*Twerski, Abraham J., *Like Yourself* *and Others Will, Too* (Englewood Cliffs, N.J.: Prentice-Hall, Inc., 1978).

important in understanding some of the genesis of alcoholism as well as some of the behavior of those close to the alcoholic.

Case 18

Dianne is a physician who was admitted to the intensive care unit in a coma from a severe overdose of sedatives. At this time, she was thirty-seven and had recently lost her job as medical director of an institution as a result of her drinking. Her drinking had progressed to the point where she would have tremors upon arising in the morning. She could not come to the office with her hands visibly shaking, nor could she settle her nerves with a drink and come to the office reeking of alcohol. Whereas some physicians confronted with this dilemma make use of tranquilizers, sedatives, or narcotics to which they have ready access, Dianne somehow did not think of pills. She did recall, however, that the label on the vanilla extract which she used in baking was 35 percent alcohol (which is 70 proof). Certainly there would be nothing incriminating about smelling of vanilla. She therefore started her day with a shot of vanilla extract, and she took along a bottle of vanilla in her purse to provide enough nips during the day to keep the tremors down; on returning from work, she could drink the real stuff.

But alcohol is alcohol, whether it be gin, beer, after-shave lotion, or vanilla extract, and Dianne's behavior deteriorated to the point where she was discharged from her position. This disappointment led to an attempt at suicide.

In the therapeutic sessions with Dianne, it was obvious that although she was an accomplished person, she had extreme feelings of inadequacy. Although she had become a physician and was the major provider for the family while also performing her functions as a wife and mother, she nevertheless did not see herself as an adequate person. One time when I said, "Tell me something positive about yourself," the response was a stony silence. I then remarked, "If you were unable to think of anything good to say about yourself, why didn't you at least say you graduated *magna cum laude* and was a Phi Beta Kappa? Certainly that is an accomplishment." With the most serene and sincere expression on her face, Dianne responded, "Doctor, when they told me that I was Phi Beta Kappa, I *knew* they had made a mistake."

Such is the intensity of a negative self-image that it will persist in gross defiance of obvious fact.

Case 19

Terry is a twenty-three-year-old woman who was referred by a psychiatrist whom she had been seeing weekly for a year for treatment of depression. The day before the referral, Terry's father had called the psychiatrist, asking whether he was aware that almost every night they had to lift her from the floor to bed after she had fallen into a drunken stupor. The psychiatrist, quite embarrassed that he had never considered that Terry might have a drinking problem, referred her for evaluation and treatment.

I found Terry to be a pleasant young woman who was stunningly attractive but quiet and withdrawn. In a conversation with her mother, I learned that

Terry was self-conscious and kept to the house a great deal. Most surprisingly, this unusually beautiful young woman considered herself physically unattractive and once remarked to her mother, "It would be easier for me to go out if I had a bag over my head."

Again, here is the presence of negative feelings in stark contradiction to obvious facts.

I hardly need stress that the pathological use of alcohol is almost invariably an escapist technique. It is evident that the alcoholic resorts to alcohol in response to stress. Understanding the role of the negative self-image makes this escapism more comprehensible, although not any more rational.

There are essentially only two possible responses to any challenge we confront. We can either *cope* with a situation or *escape* from it in any one of many ways. This is the classic "flight or fight" response.

Whether one makes the decision to cope or to escape is based on a simple formula. If one perceives oneself to be equal to or greater than the challenge, one copes. If one considers the challenge to be overwhelming, one escapes. If one finds oneself stalled on the railroad track in the path of a powerful diesel, escaping is a most healthy maneuver. Escap*ism,* however, is pathological, because the person has chosen escape as a *pattern* that pervades his life.

The person who harbors unjustified feelings of inadequacy, who perceives himself through the wrong end of a telescope, is apt to consider himself inadequate to cope with the many stresses of everyday life. He may feel so insecure about himself that many rather minor challenges appear to be so overwhelming that he feels compelled to escape them all, and often that escape is into the anesthesia or oblivion of alcohol.

Feelings of inadequacy may be pervasive, affecting every facet of a person's life, or they may be selective. In the latter case for example, a person may feel adequate and completely in charge of his work or business, but he may feel totally inadequate in social relations or as a spouse or parent. In whatever area he feels himself to be inadequate, there the tendency to escape into alcohol is apt to be greatest.

The unfortunate feature of this behavior is that since alcohol is a depressant of the central nervous system, and since alcohol in excess disturbs not only brain function but also many other bodily functions, the alcoholic eventually begins to perform poorly in precisely those areas where he felt inadequate and sought alcohol as an escape. For example, the person who feels inadequate socially and uses alcohol to escape this feeling, unwarranted as it may be, will sooner or later actually become socially inadequate as a consequence of his drinking. Starting with an ungrounded fear of being socially backward, he essentially makes a self-fulfilling prophecy come true, becoming that which he feared he already was. His feelings of social inadequacy are now reinforced by some actual deficiencies which are consequences of the drinking; and since the feelings of inadequacy are now intensified, the recourse to alcohol is apt to be even greater, resulting in a destructive self-perpetuating vicious cycle.

The same negative self-image that predisposes a person toward escapism is also operative in denial, which we discussed earlier. The more positive a person feels about himself, the easier it is for him to accept certain limitations in himself, as when he must admit that he is powerless over alcohol. The small child who feels dwarfed and impotent in a world of giant adults is apt to show off his skills, and he will proudly steer his bike with the declaration, "Look Ma, no hands." This is his way of feeling big and powerful. The adult who cannot accept help, who cannot "surrender" to the recognition that he is powerless over alcohol, who insists that he can control alcohol by himself, is desperately trying to bolster his self-image. Recognition of helplessness may be too threatening to him because of his distorted self-concept of inadequacy. We can thus see that as a result of a negative self-image, two characteristics emerge: *escapism* and *denial*, the two prime factors in alcoholism.

Self-Concept in the Alcoholic's Family

You don't have to be a Freudian to believe in unconscious motivation. There is widespread acceptance that in some way or other, our behavior is affected by feelings of which we may be unaware. Quite frequently a person will observe, "I don't know what's gotten into me that makes me do that." The books on depth psychology discuss in detail the various ideas, emotions, and even conflicts that may be going on deep in a person's psyche without his being aware of their existence, and how such unconscious thoughts manifest themselves in a person's actions.

Precisely because a person is unaware of the unconscious portion of his mind, we may not be able to establish with absolute certainty that a particular act was caused by a particular unconscious thought or feeling, but we can make some reasonable guesses. In many instances, there is quite convincing evidence pointing to the motivation in the unconscious. Very often a person will vehemently deny such unconscious motivation, especially when he would like to disown the alleged motive.

A man once remarked to his wife, "John wanted to hit me today." "How do you know he wanted to?" asked the wife. "Because he did it," the man answered. "If he hadn't wanted to, he wouldn't have done it." Sometimes all that has to be done is to watch a person's behavior, and the motivation can become quite obvious. We may not be able fully to understand the motivation, and the explanations offered by some psychologists may or may not be correct. That the reason a person gives for his own behavior is not always true is no longer in question. Rationalization, or the process whereby we give good reasons instead of the true reasons, is commonly recognized. Of course, it is quite easy for us to recognize this process in others, whereas we are often self-deceived.

Some of the difficulty arises from the fact that we generally hold ourselves responsible for our thoughts and emotions. Thus, if it is alleged that I acted in a certain way as a result of an unconscious envy, say, I am apt to resent the implication because I do not like to think of myself as being envious.

The fact is that a human being is responsible and should be held responsible for his behavior. It is a mistake to think that we are helpless pawns at the mercy of powerful instinctual impulses. Whatever the impulse may be, whether we act upon it or not is in our hands, and except for those cases in which some disease of the brain tissue destroys our controls, we have adequate behavioral restraints and options. Exerting these controls may at times be difficult and involve considerable discomfort and energy, but in the final analysis, we do have the ability to govern our own actions.

By the same token, we do not have control over the existence of instinctual thoughts and feelings and of many emotions. Some feelings are inborn and others develop as a consequence of our interaction with our environment. Some feelings, if acted upon, would be morally and ethically reprehensible, and because we consider such actions repulsive, our system represses the feelings associated with them. We would like to forget that we harbor such feelings within us, possibly because we do not feel strongly enough about our controls and are afraid that having a particular feeling might lead to its undisguised expression in behavior.

Ironically, our lack of awareness of such unacceptable feelings is apt to promote rather than inhibit their expression. For example, if I know that I harbor a great deal of anger and hostility toward a certain person, and if I have decided that for some valid reasons I do not wish to show that anger and hostility, I am in an excellent position to exert control over these emotions. Everything is aboveboard. I know what my feelings are, and because I am aware of them, I am capable of controlling them or releasing them as I deem appropriate.

If, however, I cannot accept the existence of anger and hostility within myself—as may well happen when these feelings involve someone I love or toward whom I have been taught never to bear negative feelings—then these emotions are pushed deep into my unconscious and remain outside of my awareness. Since they are instinctual, they have energy of their own, which pushes for their expression. But since I have no awareness of their presence, I can take no active measures against their expression in circuitous routes, and they may then affect my behavior in strange ways. This may be the reason a person says, "I don't know what got into me that made me do that." In such instances, "what got into me" were some feelings of which I can truthfully say "I don't know" because I was unaware of their presence; this unawareness prevented me from exerting the controls I could have used had I been alert to their presence.

It should be apparent that if we were better aware of our true feelings, needs, and impulses, we would be in much better position to have better control over our behavior as a whole. This cannot be accomplished, however, if we shudder at the thought of harboring certain feelings which we would like to think are totally foreign to us. Again, feelings *as such* are neither good nor bad; they are just there. What we *do* with them may of course be good or bad, and it is with our actions rather than our feelings that we should have the greatest concern.

With this as a background on unconscious motivation, let us turn to a phenomenon that I have observed repeatedly. A woman whose husband has been admitted to the hospital for detoxification from alcohol comes in to discuss his case. She relates the usual tale of woe about her suffering as a result of his drinking, and how it is ruining the entire home, and how she has left him several times and returned after he has promised to stop drinking, and how these promises seldom lasted for more than a week or two—and the entire litany which is so familiar to anyone who has lived with an alcoholic—closing her remarks with the assertion that he just *must* be helped to overcome this accursed condition. Since he was so horribly sick this time that he finally consented to come for help, she hopes he will now stop drinking.

After assuring the woman that we will do our utmost to steer her husband toward recovery, I caution her that experience has indicated that even after being deathly sick from alcohol, many alcoholics relapse, and some may not sober up even after multiple hospitalizations, loss of job, physical deterioration, and so on. The woman replies, "I know only too well, doctor. My father was an alcoholic, and I saw my mother take all the abuse for over thirty-five years. Nothing that she did ever helped, and he finally died of cirrhosis."

I then ask the woman, "Tell me, when you dated your husband, did he drink heavily then?" Generally the answer is, "Well, he didn't drink as much as he does now, but he did drink more than he should, and we had fights a few times when he got drunk."

"Then why," I ask, "after knowing what alcoholism is like, did you marry him?" Almost invariably the answer is something like, "I thought I could change him."

Logic would seem to indicate that a woman who had observed the horrors of living with an alcoholic would run in the opposite direction from any man who as much as looked at a bottle of beer. After observing her mother's experience, she certainly should not have had any aspirations that he would change or that she could make him change.

For all the protesting, many of these women persevere for many years, and divorce is not all that frequent. If divorce does occur and the woman remarries, it is a safe bet that she will marry another alcoholic.

After observing a number of cases with the same pattern, the only conclusion that I could reach is that some people seem to have a need for an alcoholic spouse. Why one would want an alcoholic spouse would be difficult to understand. The answer that some people are masochistic and need suffering or punishment just applies a label to the condition, and may or may not be correct. Even if true, it does not provide any explanation for the phenomenon. Why should a person have a need to suffer?

In some instances, I have been able to elucidate the following. A woman who has what I have referred to earlier as a negative self-image feels inadequate about herself. Her feelings of inadequacy, although groundless, cause her uneasiness, and she may use one of the many mechanisms to escape their discomfort.*

This woman marries a man who develops a progres-

*Abraham J. Twerski, *Like Yourself* *and Others Will, Too*. (Englewood Cliffs, N.J.: Prentice-Hall, Inc., 1978).

sive drinking problem. Prior to his excessive drinking, the husband managed the finances of the family, participated in planning their social events and, together with the wife, shared in the children's education and maturation. However, as a result of his excessive drinking and irresponsible behavior, the wife is gradually compelled to take on those responsibilities in which the husband is derelict. She may now have to keep the checkbook in balance and manage the financial affairs to see that the bills get paid on time. She may have to keep the social calendar and be responsible for remembering all the important occasions by herself. She has to carry the load of the children's school planning and be their advisor and confidant alone, since the father is usually in no shape to fulfill these functions. She may have to take possession of the car keys and do most of the driving.

What has happened is that the husband's drinking has forced the wife to assume his share of responsibility and authority in the home. This happens to be just the thing that could compensate for her feelings of low self-esteem, because she is now constantly demonstrating how adequate she really is, performing the roles of both father and mother. This is a powerful ego boost and provides a large measure of relief from the torment of low self-worth.

It is thus evident that in spite of the suffering inflicted by the husband's drinking, there is also an accompanying reward, in that the wife is able to see herself as a person of stature. This then becomes like any other transaction, where we give up something to acquire something else. If that which we wish to acquire is of sufficient value to us, we will sacrifice and pay a great price for it. Because the feelings of inadequacy can be so painful, it is possible that the woman may be willing to pay even the exorbitant price of living with an active alcoholic.

If the husband were to stop drinking, it would not be

an unmixed blessing. Whereas the wife would be free of the abuse and other consequences of his alcoholism, she also might have to surrender her position as functional head of the house. Her attitude toward his sobriety may then be as ambivalent as that toward his drinking. She is therefore capable of inadvertently doing the kinds of things that actually permit the problem to go unchecked.

The husband who returns from work at 10:00 P.M. in a half-crocked state and finds his loving and considerate wife waiting to serve his dinner is essentially being encouraged to drink. The wife who herds the children upstairs so as not to irritate daddy, who calls up the office to lie when he has a hangover, who covers up for him to his family and friends, who fails to tell the doctor that his stomach pains may be caused by all the booze he is consuming, who drives him to the office because he is too shaky to drive the car himself—any and all of these are enabling mechanisms. They prevent the alcoholic from coming face to face with the consequences of his drinking, the only thing that may get him to stop.

There is no question that the wife who employs enabling mechanisms is not doing so out of malice. No doubt she feels she is actually helping her husband by being protective of him. She has no way of knowing that her actions, which may be prolonging his drinking, are a result of her need for more self-esteem. She cannot know this because this motivation is unconscious, but, as described earlier, unconscious ideas can be very effective motivators.

The following case deals with guilt.

Case 20

Eloise began using diet pills early in her marriage. She soon discovered that in addition to controlling her appetite, the pills, which are closely related chemically to "speed," enabled her to zip through a day's work with vigor. However, as time went on she required more and more pills to get the same boost. She had already experimented with wine and had liked its tranquilizing effects. As her use of the pep pills increased, and she found herself so energized at night that she was unable to go to sleep, she turned to wine as a sedative. Soon she was into a crazy cycle of speeding up with the diet pills during the day and drinking herself to sleep at night. Occasionally, she availed herself of the tranquilizing effects of wine during the day as well. Needless to say, the home turned into a madhouse.

Andy, Eloise's husband, tried to keep some semblance of order in the house, and although he had two jobs, he did most of the washing and cleaning and some of the cooking. Eloise accused Andy of being the source of all her troubles, and Andy in order to keep peace in the house would get her the pills and the booze she requested.

Andy states that he had concurred with Eloise that he was somehow to blame for the chaos in the house, although he did not know in what way. One day, Eloise told Andy to pack his things and get out, which he promptly did, although he had no place to go.

Andy recalls standing outside with two shopping bags full of his clothes and not knowing what to do with himself. He states that he left because he was fully convinced that he was the source of all the trouble in the house.

Eloise has now recovered from her addiction and has been sober for several years. The family relationship has been restored to normal. Looking back, Andy can see how ridiculous it was for him to have assumed that he was at fault for Eloise's addiction. In his own words, "Here she is, drunk or high or both, tells me *I'm* the one with the problem, and that I should get out, and I go ahead and do it. Now tell me, who was the sicker one, she or I?"

Andy is certainly not unique; he represents a large number of spouses who mistakenly feel that they are at fault for their spouses' drinking and that the drinking spouse is an innocent victim of their deficiencies. In such a situation, they are apt to indulge the drinker as a result of misguided compassion, sympathy, and unjustified guilt.

Here too, the self-concept of the nondrinking spouse is involved. We may ask, why did Andy consider himself to be at fault? The simple answer may be that Eloise told him that he was and he believed her. Yet his acceptance of this accusation is in itself pathological, and it may be explained in one of several ways.

Andy's self-concept may have been that of a loser. We are apt to find that since childhood he was the family scapegoat and was blamed for everything. Nothing he ever did was considered right. Perhaps one or more siblings in the family were favored by either parent, and Andy was the ugly duckling. This phenomenon is not at all uncommon, and it is frequently observed by child psychiatrists and psychologists. It is a manifestation of family pathology, wherein one child becomes the ne'er-do-well. This is so impressed upon the child in his developmental years that he never conceives of himself in any other way. Obviously, this can give rise to very severe maladjustments in later life. The one that concerns us here is that if a person with this self-concept marries an alcoholic, he takes upon himself the entire blame for the spouse's drinking, and as Andy did, caters to the drinking spouse's whim. Under such circumstances, there is little chance that the drinking will cease.

There is yet another factor that may be operative in cases such as these, which represents a desperate effort by the unconscious to relieve the pain of negative self-feelings. An example from a psychotic condition may help us understand. In the condition known as paranoia, one of the cardinal symptoms is grandiosity. The patient may consider himself to be the Messiah, an emperor, chief justice of the supreme court, or some other exalted person. In other cases, there is no manifest grandiosity, but the patient may believe that the FBI and CIA are after him, that they follow him and watch his every move, and that they have wired his home and are listening to everything he says. A woman may think that men are everywhere following her and that people are taking pictures of her when she showers or bathes. Whereas these are persecutory delusions, there is a sick kind of grandiosity inherent in them. A man could hardly be insignificant if he is important enough to be an object of the FBI and CIA, who devote so much attention to him. Similarly, the woman who has delusions of being photographed nude must consider herself so attractive to someone that he wants her picture. Clearly, this desperate effort to feel important is indicative of an intolerable feeling of insignificance.

Alcoholism is replete with negative self-images, and frequently the people involved may develop fantasies of omnipotence to overcome them. The alcoholic has the omnipotent fantasy that he can control his drinking or his behavior while under the influence of alcohol, whereas there is incontrovertible evidence that he cannot. The spouse of the alcoholic has the omnipotent fantasy that he or she can control the alcoholic by some maneuver or other. But there is yet another type of omnipotence which seems to be a kind of perverse sense of power, and that is when the spouse believes that he or she is the *cause* of the drinking. This is a quite sick way of obtaining feelings of power, similar to the sick grandiosity of the paranoid; but a desperate psyche will grasp at straws. The feeling that one is powerful enough to drive another to drink may be just such a desperate attempt at overcoming intolerable feelings of impotence. To family members who consider themselves responsible for the alcoholic's drinking, I simply ask, "What makes you think that you are so powerful that you can drive a person to drink?"

If the person in the alcoholic's environment considers himself to be the cause of the drinking, he may try to cater to or protect the alcoholic, perhaps out of a feeling of guilt. However, such "kindness" to the alcoholic actually rewards the drinking, so that it progresses. The more the alcoholic drinks, the more responsible and guilty the nonalcoholic family member feels, and hence, the more protective of his whims; we thus have here a self-perpetuating vicious cycle.

A similar vicious cycle may occur when, say, the wife believes that she is responsible for her husband's drinking and tries to eliminate anything that might irritate him, lest it result in further drinking. Within a short period of time, she and the children are walking on eggs, afraid to say or do anything and essentially living in the shadow of terror. All of this is of course to no avail, because the alcoholic will continue his drinking regardless; but the tragedy is that living under such extreme restraint is apt to result in the family becoming tense and depressed, and to the drinker this can be more justification for his drinking.

This "benevolent" behavior toward the alcoholic could be eliminated if people could be helped to correct their distorted self-image. The alcoholic who develops a more positive self-image may eliminate his need to escape; the family member with a better self-image may not need to consider himself the cause of the drinking; and all the futile mechanisms resulting from considering oneself responsible for another's drinking can be dropped.

Parent-Child

Earlier, I suggested that parents are particularly prone to accommodate their alcoholic or addicted child's behavior, and by protecting him from the consequences of that behavior, they permit the addiction to persist or progress.

Case 21

> An attorney brought his eighteen-year-old son to the office for an interview. The young man had been drinking excessively since age fifteen and was now bringing ruin to the household. If something was not done about the boy, the mother was going to have a nervous breakdown. There were other children in the home who also were being hurt by the scenes and chaos created as a result of the drinking. The father realized that there was no legal way to coerce the young man into treatment, but as a doctor who specialized in alcoholism, I had to do something.

I met the son and found him to be a likeable and bright young man, who did not consider himself alcoholic. His friends all drank, and he smoked marijuana with them, but he considered himself superior because many of them also used sedatives and hallucinogens, whereas he only drank beer. He did not understand what the ruckus was all about; certainly his parents should be the last ones to point a finger, since he had seen his father tipsy on more than one occasion, and his mother was often high on the pills she was getting from the doctor. No, he did not consider himself an alcoholic, and he was not about to sign himself into any hospital since he did not need detoxification; nor would he go for several weeks to a rehabilitation program or counseling sessions.

I then called the father in and spoke with both of them. I advised the father that although the son was allegedly raising hell when intoxicated, there was no intervention possible until such time as he sought help. The father became livid with rage. There had to be something done! The family could not take his antics any longer, and they would all end up in a hospital because of him. Furthermore, the boy was a menace on the highway, having crashed his car three times in the past six months, and it was only a miracle that neither he nor someone else was killed.

I then told the father that this latest bit of information was extremely important, because since the son must have charges pending for drunken driving, we could ask the judge to stipulate that he enter a treatment program. Although coercive treatment is not ideal, it has happened that exposure to a good rehabilitation program even against one's will has proven valuable.

> The father told me that this option was not available because there were no charges pending. How come? Because the father, who is an influential lawyer, knows the right people in the court system, and he had arranged to have the charges dropped. Three times!
>
> At this point, there was another outburst of fury, but this time it was I that erupted. Here was this man, complaining bitterly and protesting that something had to be done to prevent the whole family from disintegrating into psychosis, and yet he extricated the boy from the consequences of his irresponsible behavior, not only removing the only leverage to bring him into treatment but also giving him more than tacit approval for his menacing recklessness.

This case indicates how "benevolence" can be lethal, not only to the drinker but also to countless drivers and pedestrians. It further indicates the contradiction within the family member, who may vigorously protest the alcoholic's behavior while effectively undercutting any chance of treatment.

Parents may have difficulty letting their child (of whatever age) be confronted with the consequences of his behavior because they have become habituated to the role of protector, and they are often unable to distinguish between constructive and destructive protection. In addition, a parent may see the child as an extension of himself, and we act almost as automatically to protect the child as to protect our own bodies. It may therefore take a great deal of effort to convince a parent to avoid destructive protective maneuvers.

There are several unique features in the parent-child situation. Earlier, I made a categorical statement that no one else but the drinker is responsible for his drinking.

This holds true even in the parent-child situation, yet there is no denying that parents can contribute materially to a child's alcoholism. There is considerable statistical evidence that children of alcoholics have a much higher incidence of alcoholism than children of nonalcoholics, and since children often identify with one or both parents, this finding is readily understandable. However, children do not identify with all their parent's traits, and there is still an element of selection as to which facets of a parent's character are adopted by the child.

Freud provides a helpful analogy. Suppose a victim of a robbery complains, "I was held up and robbed by the darkness and a deserted alley toward midnight." You would correct him and say, "You mean that in the darkness and the solitude of a deserted alley, some *thief* robbed you." The circumstances may indeed provide a favorable environment for the thief, but the action is perpetrated by the thief and not by the enabling circumstances. Similarly, there can be conditions that are more conducive to development of alcoholism, but the ultimate choice to drink excessively is made by the child.

Another characteristic of the parent-child relationship is the greater difficulty of accepting powerlessness. This issue is so central in both the alcoholic and the nonalcoholic family member that it is worth repeating at the risk of being redundant. The active alcoholic classically refuses to accept that he is powerless over alcohol, and the family member typically refuses to accept that he is powerless over the alcoholic.

The illusion that we can control another's behavior is highly intensified in the parent-child situation. Because of the helplessness of infants, the relationship begins in a setting in which it appears that the parent has total control of the child. The parent can pick up the infant or put him down, take him here or there, feed him or not feed him, dress him or not dress him, and in all of this the infant is apparently a totally passive partner.

This early interaction may lead the parent to believe that he can continue to manipulate the child in later life, and perhaps the tenacity with which this illusion is held is caused by a psychological need for some people to feel that they are in control of others.

Just a bit of observation will disperse the myth of parental control. One needs to go no further than the high chair and a tiny tot who sits with his lips clamped in defiance; the mother's efforts result in food in the nose, ears, and everywhere in the vicinity of the mouth except into it, because the child does not want it there, or if he does, he's not letting on. If by some measure the mother is able to maneuver the food into his mouth, he retreats to his next line of defense, which is truly formidable: He refuses to swallow, and no power on earth can force him to do so.

A second battle of wills occurs when the mother decides it is time for a bowel movement to be made in the potty instead of the diaper. The baby exerts his will, producing when he wishes and wherever he wishes, which is anywhere except the potty. Anyone who questions this as a struggle for control has only to watch the mother first sit by patiently while the baby is on the toilet seat, then sing, offer toys or sweets, and virtually turn cartwheels to achieve her goal. No human nor superhuman power can extract from the infant what he does not want to produce, and when the mother removes him from the toilet seat and back into his diaper, the desired deed is done promptly. The child has triumphed, unquestionably and irrevocably. It is clear that any subsequent decision to shift the production site from the diaper to the toilet is the child's and the child's alone.

These manifestations of defiance occur long before the child can speak fluently or think in sophisticated terms. He has already asserted his independence, and as his knowledge, skills, and wisdom increase, he is not apt to relinquish his sovereignty. He may soon realize that it is more expedient to make some tradeoffs, that some things he wants will be more forthcoming if he fulfills his parents' wishes. His compliance with parental wishes gives the superficial appearance that he is controlled by the parent; but the child knows the truth, and only the parents—deluded by their aspirations to be in control—imagine that it is indeed so. The child bides his time, and when circumstances turn somewhat in his favor, he once again openly asserts the self-determination that he had never truly surrendered.

The reality, then, is that we do not have control over our children, much as we would love to believe otherwise. When they are dependent on parents in one or more ways, there is a degree of leverage in the bargaining: If you do or don't do thus and so, you will or will not get this or that. When the child can afford to give up the rewards of compliance, he may choose to assert his independence; the only thing parents can do then is to try to renegotiate a new agreement, which generally means offering additional rewards or threatening new deprivations—which is what the mythical parental "controls" consist of.

10

Child-Parent

Case 22

Jane, Ed, and Bonnie came to the office for help with their mother, who had become a heavy drinker. Widowed for six years, she had been a "moderate" drinker when her husband was alive. Since his death, she had remained virtually secluded in the house. She had never had many friends even while her husband was living, and her entire existence had centered about him. After his death, she became much more demanding of the children, not only to take her shopping or to the doctor, but to provide her with fairly constant companionship.

Jane and Ed were married, with families of their own. Bonnie still lived with her mother, but her job took her out of town frequently, trips which the mother bitterly resented because she remained alone. Bonnie was seriously involved in a romance, and the mother perceived the possibility of her marriage as a threat of desertion.

The pattern that had developed was that when the mother drank, she would either call up the children and cry or call some friends of the family and let them know how terribly lonely she was because the children neglected her. If ever Jane and Ed did not visit for a few days, Bonnie might come home from a trip to find the house in a mess and the mother in a drunken stupor. All the children repeatedly heard the phrase, "If you didn't leave me alone so much, I wouldn't drink."

Bonnie began to feel so responsible for her mother's drinking that she was thinking of quitting her job and looking for work that would not take her out of town; she was also considering breaking off with her fiancé because of her mother's resentment.

Jane and Ed both said that their own family lives were deteriorating, because every time their mother would call for them to come, they felt obligated to do so regardless of what they had planned for their own families. If they did not respond to her call because of some activity of their own, they were so guilt-ridden and frustrated that she might drink because of them that they could not enjoy themselves. Ed's wife and Jane's husband were protesting that they could not put up with the mother's repeated destruction of their planned events. Ed, Jane, and Bonnie were all at their wits' end, feeling trapped and powerless.

This case hardly calls for psychological interpretation. However she had arrived at alcohol excess, the mother was now using her drinking as a powerful lever to control the family. Since the children generally responded to her manipulations, they were reinforced. Nobody discontinues a maneuver that is effective. Obviously, nothing the children did reduced their mother's drinking, and the progressive course was going to result not only in her deterioration but also in serious harm to all the children and their families.

Ethically and morally, children have certain obligations toward their parents. If children are derelict in fulfilling just obligations they have committed a wrong, and to that extent they should indeed feel guilty and take appropriate steps to make amends. Not all guilt is pathological. Indeed, healthy guilt over misdeeds is an important factor in developing and maintaining responsible human behavior. But not all guilt is healthy, as when someone feels guilty because he could not comply with unreasonable and unrealistic demands. The guilt that consumed Jane, Ed, and Bonnie is an example of unhealthy guilt, because the mother's demands were absurd. At first glance, it appears that the children were trying to be kind to their mother, yet it is obvious that their benevolence was working to her detriment.

If we focus more precisely on this example, we may see a theme that is pervasive in most instances of lethal benevolence. The children's deference to their mother's wishes, which essentially encouraged her drinking, did not arise out of pure concern for her true needs but rather from the desire to prevent feelings of guilt. Refusing to comply with the mother's requests, regardless of how unjust they may have been, would have left them with a very uncomfortable emotion. The motivation to comply therefore originated from the wish to avoid uncomfortable feelings. What appears superficially as an altruistic act can now be seen as a self-directed act, whose goal is to avoid one's own discomfort.

This is the hallmark of virtually all behavior that has been referred to as *lethal benevolence*, whether between spouses, parents and children, doctors and patients, or any other people in a relationship. On the surface, the behavior appears to be motivated by concern for the drinker, but deeper analysis will show that it is really quite self-oriented. As mentioned in the Introduction, true concern for the drinker will be more like the mother's concern for the sick infant who needs an injection of penicillin. She will no doubt feel very distressed at having to hold a crying and struggling baby while the doctor jabs him with a painful needle, but her knowledge that she is helping the child enables her to provide true protection.

What might Ed, Jane, and Bonnie have done? It is generally easier to advise what *not* to do, but each case must be considered according to its particular circumstances. In this case, the children should all meet together with their mother, advising her that Bonnie has a life of her own which she is going to pursue and that Ed and Jane would be glad to have the mother share as much of their own family lives as is reasonable. They could assure the mother of their love for her, but also that they would not allow their own pursuits to be dominated by her drinking or threats thereof. They could explain that if she accepted treatment for her drinking and recovered, her part in their lives and families would be greatly enhanced. On the other hand, if she rejected treatment and continued her destructive drinking, she must realize that there was really no sense in allowing themselves to be destroyed along with her and that they simply would not respond to her calls. Once such a course has been determined, the children would then have to stand firm in its implementation.

This might appear superficially to be an insensitive if not a disrespectful attitude toward a parent. However, one of the criticisms of the bureaucratic system is that it operates on the philosophy, "If what you are doing isn't working, do more of the same." The mother's health, life, and welfare were *not* being promoted by yielding to her alcoholism. A firm resistance to the alcoholic manipulation could provide the only hope for recovery. As will be pointed out later, such an approach is not without risk, but it should be apparent that the risk of reinforcing the alcoholism is even greater.

11

On the Job

In the past several years, there has been a movement that holds great promise for rescuing perhaps hundreds of thousands of people, and millions of their loved ones, from the ravages of alcoholism. Many major industries have made significant strides in developing policies on alcoholism for their firms, and insurance underwriters in ever growing numbers are covering hospitalization and rehabilitative services. Labor unions—recognizing that protection of a member's job while his health and personality deteriorate is not really a favor—are taking a more aggressive stand on urging or insisting on treatment for alcoholism. These efforts on the part of both labor and management are most laudable. However, they are really only a beginning, and more comprehensive programs must be developed both at the grass roots and corporate levels.

Job leverage is one of the most potent forces available to induce an alcoholic to accept treatment. People who have not sought help because of imminent loss of family or serious health problems have responded positively to the threat of dismissal. Especially for the male in western culture, being able to earn a living may be of much greater ego importance than anything else. The man who does not stop drinking when his wife and children leave but does so when his job is in jeopardy does not necessarily love his family less than his job. Rather, his identity as a man may be contingent on his being a wage earner, and the loss of identity may be psychologically more devastating than loss of love.

In spite of the new trend in industrial treatment of alcoholism, there is still a very strong tendency to overlook it. Although an employee's personal life is off limits for the employer, it does not take very long before alcoholic excess stops being purely a personal problem and begins to affect job performance, and the latter is very much within the employer's area of concern. The problems presented by absenteeism, with the disruption of efficiency, are exceeded only by the problems of "on-the-job absenteeism." Lack of reliability, poor quality, and the much higher incidence of accidents because an employee is under the influence of alcohol or has a hangover of greater or lesser intensity have resulted in costs to industry of many billions of dollars annually.

Nevertheless there is still a great deal of hesitancy to intervene even when an employee's alcoholism is affecting his job. The employee's superior, whether line supervisor or higher echelon executive, is apt to overlook the behavior, accept ridiculous and patently false excuses, or at the most mention his concern to the employee and extract a promise that it will not happen again. Since such promises cannot possibly be fulfilled, the behavior recurs; eventually a reprimand is issued, which may for a varying period of time cause the employee not to stop drinking but to exercise enough discretion so that it does not affect his work. Eventually, this maneuver fails, and the alcoholic's behavior ultimately leads to disciplinary action of one type or another or dismissal from the job.

Covering up for an employee is often due to a superior's ill-advised sense of loyalty. The relationship of the superior to the employee is not unlike that of the parent to the child, with its potential for destructive protection. Sometimes the superior's own excessive drinking makes him reluctant to take more aggressive steps. Often he shares in the delusion that alcoholism can be corrected by willpower alone, believing that a fatherly reprimand or threat of dismissal can have a long-term effect on the drinking.

Case 23

John was admitted into an alcoholism rehabilitation center after a ten-week hospitalization for delirium tremens and severe liver failure. Even after intensive treatment in a general hospital for ten weeks, John looked more ready for admission to a hospital than discharge. His face was drawn, with sunken cheeks and yellowish eyeballs; his fluid-laden abdomen protruded like that of a woman in advanced pregnancy; and his swollen ankles overhung his shoes. His thought processes were hazy, and he had difficulty in following directions and sometimes even in finding his room. At this time, John was fifty-three years old.

John had been with his firm for nineteen years in various sales capacities. In retrospect, his excessive use of alcohol had existed even before he joined the firm. His involvement in sales provided fertile grounds not only for drinking but also for rationalizing it; "You can't sell unless you drink with the customer."

John had been successful in his job and had received numerous bonuses and several promotions. About six years before his admission for treatment, the first actual interference with work occurred (to the best of John's recollection). He was to have been at a business meeting out of town on a Monday morning. He checked into a motel on Sunday, drank heavily that night, and awoke at 1:00 p.m. on Monday. As soon as he could mobilize himself, he called his business contacts and coughed like crazy into the phone. He stated that he had come down with a fever of 103 degrees, had been given a shot of penicillin and a sedative by a physician, and in his run-down state must have been overdrugged. He apologized for the inconvenience and offered to reschedule the meeting for the following morning. The home office did not learn of the incident, and the people whom he was to meet never questioned how a person could be so sick with fever and a violent cough on Monday and yet look quite well on Tuesday. However, his health was clearly none of their business, and the whole incident went by unremarked.

During the next few years, there were several occasions when John's superior spoke to him about his drinking. At times, John returned from extended lunch periods with obvious signs of drunkenness, and on at least two occasions, his boss told him in a very friendly way to cut his lunch-time drink down to one martini. Once a female employee reported him for having made obscene remarks. His boss spoke to him about the complaint, which he completely denied. His denial may have been sincere, because in all likelihood he had had a blackout during the event. His boss told him this act was out of character and raised the question of whether he might not have been uninhibited because of drinking. John of course denied the drinking but was sufficiently frightened to vow never to touch another drop, which he didn't—for three months.

John resumed drinking after the dry interval at a increasing rate. Once he had a total blackout during the proceedings of a business meeting on which he was to report to the office. However, he had become aware of his propensity to forget and had taken the precaution of writing everything down in detail as a meeting progressed. By referring to his carefully recorded notes, he avoided the consequences of his blackouts, until the time when he misplaced his notes while under the influence of alcohol and could not give the office any information about what had occurred. This time, the boss told him that his drinking would absolutely have to stop *or else.* John made another solemn promise, indicating to his boss that he had already abstained once completely for several months and so there was no problem in stopping now. This time the abstinence lasted for eight weeks.

The *coup de grace* came at a meeting of district sales managers at which John was to make a presentation. By this time, he had returned to "nipping" in an attempt to avoid getting drunk. The day before the meeting, he drank heavily, and the following morning he awoke with tremors. In order to steady himself, he took a few drinks before the meeting; he then proceeded to make a spectacle of himself, which upset the whole gathering and resulted in his having to be bodily removed from the room, which was not accomplished without a struggle. Immediately thereafter he was fired.

His response to the loss of his job was of course predictable, resulting in his eventual hospitalization in a condition closer to death than to life. Anyone who saw John upon his admission to the rehabilitation program would have no doubt that his firm's tolerance of his drinking was anything but kind.

Case 24

Elmer is a forty-nine-year-old factory worker admitted to an alcoholism rehabilitation program on referral of the plant physician. One year earlier, Elmer had undergone a port-caval procedure because of advanced cirrhosis of the liver.

(A port-caval shunt, a difficult surgical procedure, is essentially a liver bypass. Because of the obstruction of blood flow through the liver as a result of cirrhosis, the enormous quantity of blood that normally flows smoothly through the liver backs up and finds circuitous detours back to the heart. Some of these detours are through tiny blood vessels, which are thereby forced to expand. The balooning of these vessels makes them prone to rupture, possibly resulting in serious and often fatal hemorrhage. The purpose of the post-caval shunt is to create a better detour to take the pressure off the small blood vessels and prevent hemorrhage. It is a kind of last ditch attempt and does nothing to correct the liver disease.)

Elmer had returned to work after recovering from the surgery. He was always tired, even early in the day. In spite of his serious liver disease and the warning that any alcohol could kill him, Elmer stayed off alcohol for only three months after discharge from the hospital. His relapse into drinking led to examination by the company doctor and a referral for treatment.

Elmer had been with the company for many years. He had been a heavy drinker since he could remember. Sporadic calling in sick had occurred many years back and had never prompted any questioning, but gradually his absenteeism became more severe. "I never went to work drunk. I just didn't go in." Elmer's supervisor talked with him on several occasions about his absenteeism. "Hell, he knew I drank. Half the time he'd be drinking with me at the bar, only it didn't affect him the way it did me. Maybe I drank more than him. He told me I'd better get into shape and cut down my drinking." On one occasion Elmer had a disciplinary hearing and was suspended for one week without pay. "The year before the operation, I missed seventy-six days."

About three years before his admission for rehabilitation, Elmer's wife divorced him. "I can't blame the woman. She's a good woman, and she put up with a lot of my craziness. I miss her, and I miss my kids, too, but I know they're never going to come back."

I asked Elmer what he would have done had he been the supervisor and had an employee like himself. "I don't know. I think I would've got on his tail and gotten him to a place like this earlier. But it's hard to say. He covered up for me because he liked me, and when you like a guy, it's hard to put the screws on. You don't want to cost a guy his job."

The supervisor, with all good intentions, had "liked" Elmer into loss of his wife and children, into near-fatal liver disease from which he was still not recovered, and ultimately into loss of the job that he had hoped to save. At this point, Elmer was no longer physically capable of working, and even if he no longer drank, he would have to subsist on some type of disability income.

Fortunately, the recent trend in industrial treatment of alcoholism may help avoid tragic cases like that of Elmer. Companies have begun to develop policies on alcoholism, recognizing it as an illness for which treatment is available, providing health benefits for this condition as for any other health problem, and assuring job security for the employee whose alcoholism is checked. Some companies have comprehensive, aggressive programs, with methods for identifying alcoholics and a smoothly functioning system of referral and follow-up. Other companies only give lip service to the problem, but otherwise it is business as usual. Continued educational efforts at all levels, big business and small business, management and labor, is vitally necessary. When the employee's alcoholism is recognized and appropriately treated, everybody wins; when it is overlooked, everybody loses—in dollars, in suffering, and in lives.

12

The Pastoral Counselor

The clergyman can play a pivotal role in alcoholism. It should be remembered, however, that a *pivot* is something about which something else turns. The turn can be in the wrong as well as in the right direction, or there can be a constant revolving movement without anyone getting anywhere.

The pastor holds a unique position. Of all therapists and counselors, he is virtually the only one who does not have to wait for the patient or client to come to him. It is perfectly legitimate and acceptable for the priest, minister, or rabbi to make a pastoral call without prior invitation, and he can utilize this opportunity to apprise the family of his observation that they have a problem of which they may be unaware or with which they may be at a loss to cope effectively. The prestige and authority of the pastor can be a powerful force for constructive change, and trust and confidence in the clergyman are of inestimable value.

It seems to be a law of nature that any potent force for good can also be correspondingly harmful if not applied properly. It is therefore extremely important to be aware of the possible pitfalls of clerical intervention, because misguided pastoral involvement can result in undesirable consequences.

Benevolence is a virtue that receives a great deal of emphasis in religion, sometimes to the point of self-sacrifice and even to the point of martyrdom. It is therefore easily understood how a pastor, imbued with enthusiasm for acts of benevolence, may perform or counsel others to perform acts which appear to be benevolent but which are actually detrimental to the alcoholic's recovery. It may take a great deal of enlightenment concerning the dynamics of alcoholism to convince a well-meaning pastor that his good intentions may be contributing to prolongation of the problem.

Guilt and its expiation are the stuff of which much of religious activity is comprised. In the alcoholic, guilt and remorse are part and parcel of the vicious cycle of addiction. It is easy to confuse the alcoholic guilt and remorse with the healthy religious variety, and many a pastor has been taken in by the self-flagellating alcoholic whose guilt feelings are soon to be relieved by the anesthetic effect of alcohol.

The pastor who does not recognize the pathology of alcoholic dependency may become part of a domino reaction wherein the alcoholic becomes dependent on the spouse, who then depletes himself or herself by feeding the alcoholic's demands, and the exhausted spouse then seeks fulfillment of his or her own needs by becoming dependent on the pastor. The pastor, feeling that his role obligates him to be all things to all people, may respond to these incessant demands. As long as the needs of pathological dependency are met, no growth occurs in either the alcoholic or the spouse, and when there is no personality growth, deterioration soon sets in.

To the religious leader the sanctity of family integrity has always been of overriding importance, and many times couples have been advised to tolerate a great deal of unpleasantness in order to avoid the disaster of a broken home. Although there is no minimizing the disruptive effects of a marital separation, it must nevertheless be realized that they may possibly be surpassed by those caused by alcohol or drug abuse. A therapist or counselor, whether secular or religious, should not urge separation, on the principle that this is a decision that can be reached only by the participant and not by an outsider, no matter how experienced or wise. By the same reasoning, the decision to reconcile or not to separate is again one that should come from within. The function of the counselor is to clarify issues and clear away the distortion and confusion so that the person involved may see the situation more objectively and avoid being influenced by essentially irrelevant factors.

Case 25

Caroline was back in the pastor's study. She had left Ed for the third time three weeks earlier and, with their two children, had moved to her parents' home. Ed was a "periodic" drinker, who would go for weeks and even months without a single drink but abruptly and without apparent reason go out on a binge. Then he would come home and behave like a madman, shouting obscenities at Caroline and the children, pushing them around, and throwing things in the house. After sobering up, he would be full of remorse and apologize profusely, buy gifts for the family, and swear this would never happen again. Since it always did happen again, Caroline had left him twice previously.

Ed held an important position in the bank and was a prominent citizen. He did not consider himself an alcoholic because he did not drink every day, and in fact had gone as long as five months without a drink. Caroline described their alcohol-free intervals as "beautiful," since Ed was the sweetest and most considerate man a woman could ask for; until he drank, that is. Alcohol would turn him into an uncontrollable monster. Caroline was convinced Ed had a "split personality" and also shared his view that a person who had long intervals of abstinence could not be alcoholic.

The incident that precipitated the most recent separation was that on the latest binge Ed had virtually demolished the house, breaking fixtures and furniture, and had shot holes in the walls with his gun. Caroline had been almost paralyzed with fear but had managed to get the children to a neighbor's home for safety. She had not called the police because she was afraid this would ruin Ed's standing in the community.

After recovering from the binge, Ed was shocked at the appearance of the house and had no memory of his behavior. By the process of exclusion, he had to accept that it was he rather than a localized tornado that had turned the house into a shambles. He ran to Caroline, who refused to see him. He then went to the pastor before whom he cried with remorse. He had now realized how sick he was. Previously he had not believed Caroline's accounts of his behavior while he was intoxicated, but now the facts were irrefutable. He could not imagine how he could have been capable of such destruction There was no question now that he would never again allow himself to take even a single drink. No, he would not consider going to Alcoholics Anonymous for two reasons. First, he was not really an alcoholic because he had long periods of unassisted abstinence and sobriety. Second, the community was a relatively small one, and there was no way to prevent the secret of his AA attendance from becoming known, which would ruin his status as one of the social pillars of the community. He was uncertain about seeing a psychiatrist, because there was really nothing mentally wrong with him, as was demonstrated by his perfectly exemplary behavior during the periods of abstinence. The only "craziness" occurred during the drunken binges, and since these were now gone forever, he didn't need a psychiatrist to tell him not to drink. Nevertheless, if it would help get Caroline back, he would consent to see a psychiatrist.

Caroline was wary. She had been through this pattern too many times, and the tears and promises were now familiar. The drunken behavior was getting progressively worse, and the next time someone might get killed. It was miraculous that someone hadn't been killed or seriously injured this last time.

The pastor told Caroline how Ed had been to see him and had cried bitterly with sincere remorse. He had never seen anyone with such a profound sense of guilt. Ed had truly been shocked into reality by the full realization of his behavior, he said, which is something that he had never previously accepted. Caroline had to admit that Ed was a loving father, and continued separation from the children could be harmful to them, the pastor said. He said that Ed was a strong-willed person, and now that he had set his mind never to drink again, even on New Year's Eve as Ed had said, there was no longer any reason for worry. Finally, Ed had agreed to see a psychiatrist if Caroline so wished, and that should certainly remove the last vestige of doubt about Ed's sincerity.

The pastor urged Caroline to return home and give Ed the encouragement and will to avoid further drinking.

There is certainly no question about the wholesomeness of the pastor's intentions, but equally no question about his total misunderstanding of alcoholism. Even Ed had recognized that his behavior was sick. Sick behavior calls for treatment, not for promises or assertion of will power. No one would accept a person's promise that he would never have another attack of pneumonia, nor an assertion of willpower to prevent coughing. However, Ed's offer to see a psychiatrist was only to placate Caroline, and not because Ed recognized a need for treatment. His realization that he had to be sick to have behaved as he did was a fleeting, momentary insight which was promptly forgotten. Instead of concentrating on the fact that Ed was sick and that vigorous therapy was mandatory for so serious a condition, the pastor unwittingly allied himself with all of Ed's pathology, which would have led to continued disaster.

Finally, there is the old bugaboo which seems to appear in all alcoholics: feelings of omnipotence. Perhaps the clergyman, who may consider himself the vicar of God and as such a representative of the true omnipotent Being, may sometimes have difficulties in recognizing his limitations. One manifestation of his feeling of omnipotence in this case is making decisions for Caroline and urging her to a specific course. Even if he were unaware of the characteristics of alcoholic behavior—with the complete worthlessness of this man's heart-rending remorse, profound guilt, and sacred promises—the pastor should have withheld decision making. In response to the question, "What do you think I should do," the pastor could have said something to the effect of

"I really can't tell you what you should do. You are the one who must make your decisions and take responsibility for them. I can only help you look at all the issues that should go into the decision-making process so that you can consider them without distortion for some emotional or various external pressures." When the therapist sets a pattern of not controlling the family, the family members are more apt to see that they should not try to control the alcoholic, and perhaps even the alcoholic can eventually get a more realistic grasp on his fantasy about controlling alcohol.

Driving and Alcohol

Nowhere is the phenomenon of lethal benevolence as painfully and strikingly apparent as in our management of the intoxicated motorist. Here there is no need to delve into psychological theories or philosophical arguments to make the point. There is even no need for illustrative examples. All of us are confronted daily in one way or another with stark evidence of the deadliness of the drunken driver, by the daily reports of traffic fatalities and the gruesome pictures of mangled automobiles. Yet we remain ambivalent toward the problem, allowing the carnage to continue.

It has been said that the media exerted a powerful and decisive force in arousing the country's opposition to the Vietnam war by repeatedly focusing the television cameras on the bloody scenes of the battlefield and graphically affecting the public conscience with color photos in newspapers and magazines of maimed and disfigured innocent children. Yet when the television and newspaper cameras arrive at an automobile accident, where crews are trying to extricate humans or the mangled bodies of humans from masses of twisted metal, the photographers seem to turn away from the gruesome features.

Where are the anticarnage pickets? Where are the protestors? Where are the marches on Washington or the state capitols? Where is the persistent pressuring of legislators? Where are the rallies and public demonstrations?

If these lines appear impassioned, it is perhaps because as a physician I have had much exposure to the ravages of drunken driving. From the emergency room with the mauled victims of intoxicated drivers, to the psychological treatment of families who have been devastated by loss of a father, mother, or child, the immeasurable horror and suffering observed cannot allow an attitude of indifference.

Society's attitude toward drunken driving is perhaps representative of the attitudes toward alcoholism as a whole, some of which have been described in previous chapters. We condemn it, we preach against it, we threaten, we accept empty pledges, and we effectively allow the deadly process to continue.

The statistics are staggering, and yet may represent only the tip of the iceberg. The available figures refer only to recognized use of alcohol by the driver. Countless motorists drive under the same numbing effect of the various tranquilizers and sedatives, both prescribed and over the counter, which dull the driver's alertness and impair his reflexes; yet there is no detection of these.

Over 50 percent of all traffic fatalities involve a driver with sufficient alcohol in the blood stream to impair his driving. Of the remaining 50 percent, we have no idea how many are under the influences of some other mind-altering chemical. There are more deaths caused by alcohol-related accidents than those in all the United States' wars combined. Yet, there are no rallies, no protests, and no marches.

The current court system for handling the drunken driver is grossly inept. The combination of legal niceties, long delays before trial, plea bargaining, and misguided sympathy add up to a system that allows the carnage to run rampant. We all know of cases such as the following: the "considerate" officer who did not report that the young woman whose car was wrapped around a telephone pole was clearly intoxicated because "just looking at the car, she had suffered enough, and besides, she hadn't hurt anyone." He was indeed very kind to this once beautiful young woman, whose next accident from drunken driving resulted in loss of an eye and unattractive facial distortion. As she goes through much painful plastic surgery which will never restore her to her natural beauty, she will certainly not be grateful to the officer for his ill-fated "kindness."

Or take the sympathy of the judge and/or jury who will not revoke a person's license for drunken driving because it will deprive him of his livelihood. Why is his livelihood any more sacred than that of the family whose provider was cut down by a drunken driver? Why does his livelihood take precedence over someone else's very life?

I do not presume to have the precise formula for eradicating this problem. There are thousands of articles and research projects on the subject and numerous cases in various jurisdictions. The one thing that is clear is that whatever we are doing now about the problem, whether in public education, treatment, or punishment, is simply tokenism.

The issue here is not a person's drinking. An individual may well have the constitutional right to drink himself into oblivion, but he does not have the right to wield a potentially lethal vehicle while under the effects of alcohol. In many cases, we may not be dealing with a problem of alcoholism but that of the irresponsibility of drunken driving.

There may well be effective steps that could be taken, but these may have to be far more radical than those in operation at present. If certain types of cases respond to a punitive deterrent approach, then we should not hesitate to invoke the necessary disciplinary actions. It may seem harsh to make a single drunken driving offense punishable by irrevocable and permanent loss of license, but if this can be shown to be effective, then it should be adopted. It may seem too demanding to make comprehensive treatment mandatory when the driver is determined to be alcoholic, but if that is what is necessary, that is what should be done. It may appear cumbersome to implement a program in which a drunken driver must appear *daily* before an officer of the law and in the latter's presence swallow a tablet of disulfuram, which will remove his ability to drink for the next few days, but if that is effective, that is what should be done.

Perhaps what is needed is a national convention of authorities in the various fields relating to alcohol and traffic safety to hammer out a policy that will be effective regardless of its cost or inconveniences. This should be followed by a marathon congressional session wherein an effective and nationally uniform program should be adopted, with the necessary changes in laws, procedures, educational efforts, and treatment to implement the program. Such a massive effort could result only if the problems were accorded top priority. But like the spouse who complains bitterly about her suffering, yet is unwilling to take the measures to save herself and eliminate the enabling mechanism, our society is not apt to move in this direction.

14

Doctor-Patient

There are two factors that appear to underlie the phenomenon of lethal benevolence. One factor, or rather group of factors, is the personality element operative in the nonalcoholic in the drinker's environment, which contributes to neglect or condonation of the problem in one way or another. The second factor is ignorance. Most people do not know or perhaps do not wish to know the facts about untreated alcoholism.

One area where lack of knowledge about alcoholism is most dangerous and least forgivable is medicine. Doctors are often the first to detect the condition, and they have the power which, if properly used, could affect the patient most constructively. It is a grievous fault that many physicians do not have adequate knowledge about alcoholism.

I attended an excellent medical school. I learned about some exotic diseases that I would rarely, if ever, see in my lifetime, no matter what specialty I chose. I learned nothing about alcoholism or addiction, which is directly or indirectly involved in many conditions that bring a person to the attention of a physician. I learned how to treat some of the sequelae of alcoholism, such as delerium tremens, liver failure, and the like, but nothing about the disease itself. I do not believe that other medical schools were substantially different from mine, nor that the situation is really that much different now than twenty-five years ago.

I then entered a psychiatric residency training program, one of the finest in the country. There was no formal alcoholism service in the psychiatric hospital where I trained, and generally alcoholics were not admitted because they were not considered "good teaching cases." I learned little about alcoholism in the regular curriculum, and the little that was taught was wrong.

The theory that alcoholic drinking is a symptom of an underlying emotional disorder and should be treated like any other psychological symptom—that is, investigating its origin, then treating the underlying cause—simply does not work in most cases. The alcoholic will be only too happy to embark on a course of treatment that promises to remove his need for alcohol, because the implication is that until such time as the cause is discovered and removed by psychotherapy, he can continue to drink. This is an eternal cop-out, because no psychotherapy of any kind is going to be effective while the patient continues dousing his brain with alcohol.

Alcohol is a powerful central nervous system depressant that profoundly affects brain-cell function. It is inconceivable that anyone would try to understand what is going on inside the brain while it is repeatedly being bludgeoned with a chemical sledgehammer.

Furthermore, alcoholics are the world's most competent projectors and rationalizers. All of us have had parents, and as good as they may have been, none were angels. A parent is either dominant or passive; hence only four combinations are possible. One either had two dominant parents, two passive parents, a dominant father and passive mother, or a passive father and dominant mother. In using psychotherapy with an alcoholic, it will come to light that he had one of these parental configurations. To the alcoholic, this discovery is more than adequate justification for his drinking. He will now indulge in self-pity for being the innocent victim of pathological parenting, and such self-pity is worth about a fifth a day.

Nowhere in my psychiatric training was I exposed to any method of managing the alcoholic that has had any success. Certainly the professionals were not going to defer to a group of lay people in Alcoholics Anonymous. So the whole issue of alcoholism was just ignored, or better yet, its existence was denied. *Denial* is as prevalent in the medical profession as it is in the alcoholic.

Nowhere in my training was I advised of the phenomenon of *cross-addiction:* That is, a person who is addicted to alcohol will in all likelihood use any mind-altering chemical in the same fashion, and that therefore prescribing a tranquilizer, sedative, or pain-killer for an alcoholic is apt to result in his addiction to any or all of these substances.

Physicians are people who want to help. If they did not have the need to relieve suffering they probably would not have chosen medicine as a career. There are other professions that are equally as lucrative and less demanding. To invest twelve or more grueling years in education before one can earn a decent living, one is motivated by more than economic considerations, and one of the prime motivations is the need to be a helper, a reliever, a soother.

It is therefore almost a reflex action for a physician to prescribe a sedative for insomnia, a tranquilizer for nervousness, or a potent analgesic for pain. It is most difficult for a physician to tell a patient that he must learn how to live with his discomfort. The physician sees this as a gross dereliction on his part. He feels he is there to help and should do something to provide relief. Furthermore, why should he not prescribe an effective medication? No one in medical school ever taught him that these medications are highly addictive. Most of the doctor's information about new drugs comes from the pharmaceutical company salesman, who promotes the company's often misleading advertisement of the drug's safety. Some of the worst addictions we see clinically are to drugs that have been proclaimed as breakthroughs in the management of insomnia and pain because they are "nonbarbiturate sedatives" or "nonopiate analgesics." Indeed they are. They are worse than the barbiturates and opiates, to whose potential harm we were at least somewhat alerted.

Many physicians do not know how to take an alcoholic history. They know that when they ask a patient about his chest pain or bowels they generally get reliable information upon which to base a diagnosis. Nothing could be more different in cases of alcoholism. The active alcoholic simply does not, and perhaps cannot, tell the truth about the extent of his use of alcohol or pills. If the condition is at all suspected, as it should be much more often, additional data may have to be sought from family members, closer attention paid to interpretation of laboratory tests, and more time spent with the patient in skillful interviewing, which might elicit more reliable information.

Finally, most physicians are nice people who do not like to insult anyone, especially someone who has come to them for help. If the physician considers alcoholism to be a character weakness, a moral deterioration, a lack of willpower, or any other condition with a derogatory connotation, he is apt not to make the correct diagnosis because he does not want to offend the patient: a classic example of misguided benevolence.

Case 26

Raymond was a thirty-five-year-old executive who was admitted for detoxification from alcohol. He had suffered extensive liver damage with several convulsions. After detoxification, he was urged into AA and eventually enjoyed sobriety.

The corporation for which Raymond worked requested biannual medical evaluations. At the time of reexamination, Raymond had been sober more than one year, and the examining physician remarked, "Ray, I never thought I'd see you alive."

After Raymond related the story of his recovery, the doctor asked, "In retrospect, what could I have done to have helped you?"

"You could have told me I was alcoholic," Raymond said. The doctor shook his head. "I'd rather have told you you had cancer," he said. "With cancer, at least I could have given you a statistic as to your chances. With alcoholism, I've never seen one of them come back, and you must remember, I too have an ego."

The frankness of this physician is refreshing, but it reveals what is probably often not said or even considered. A physician may be reluctant to make a diagnosis of a condition for which he feels he has nothing to offer. Probably his only contact with alcoholics is when they require medical attention for either detoxification or some physical complication resulting from their drinking. He simply may not have had exposure to those alcoholics who have recovered. This gross lack of sophistication in alcoholism is attributable primarily to the lack of awareness or denial among those responsible for medical education.

There are nevertheless indications of progress. Postgraduate seminars on alcoholism are now increasingly available, and many prestigious medical journals are featuring articles on the subject. Finally, the recent advances in the number of cases of alcoholism and addiction found among physicians themselves and provision of treatment have helped bring the problem as a whole before the eyes of the medical profession.

The password is alertness, and one must remember the ubiquity and toxicity of alcohol. In bygone years, syphilis was considered "the great masquerader"; that is, it could mimic virtually every disease. Today that title should be applied to alcoholism, which may be responsible for various physical as well as emotional diseases and symptoms. The physician who diagnoses peptic ulcer, diabetes, or hypertension may be so impressed with the symptoms of these conditions that he does not reflect that their etiology or aggravating factor may be alcoholism. The psychiatrist whose patient presents symptoms of anxiety, depression, or even manic-depressive mood swings may not realize that these might be manifestations of alcohol or drug abuse.

Case 27

> Donna was a forty-two-year-old woman who came to see a psychiatrist because of anxiety and depression of many years duration. She had already been treated by several psychiatrists and had been hospitalized once following an overdose, which resulted in a coma and a tracheostomy. After taking a history and making a diagnosis of agitated depression, the latest psychiatrist she consulted prescribed an antidepressant and a tranquilizer.
>
> Donna saw the psychiatrist once a week. Her symptoms fluctuated, and there was no pattern of pro-

gressive recovery. On several occasions, she was brought to the emergency room with various bruises or injuries following falls; eventually, the psychiatrist realized that she was abusing sedatives and ordered her to abstain from their use, but he continued the antidepressants.

Physical problems of various kinds developed, and Donna was hospitalized for evaluation. Her liver function tests were abnormal, for which there was no explanation. Donna insisted she never drank more than an occasional bottle of beer. During her workup in the hospital, Donna had an allergic reaction to one of the chemicals used in a test and had a cardiac arrest, from which she was resuscitated with a second tracheostomy.

The psychiatric management continued for several years, and it wasn't until after the cardiac arrest that the psychiatrist learned from Donna's husband that she drank heavily and regularly, abstaining the day of her appointment to prevent the psychiatrist from recognizing the truth. We have here an unwitting collusion between the psychiatrist, who overlooked the obvious, and the husband, who did not tell the psychiatrist what was going on. As a consequence, everyone involved, but primarily Donna, suffered considerably.

I am most intimately familiar with the details of this case because, as I must painfully admit, I was the psychiatrist and Donna was my patient. The psychiatrists whom she had previously consulted had not made the correct diagnosis, but this does not excuse my error. Furthermore, I was by this time quite involved in the treatment of alcoholism and should have known better. This case only demonstrates the treacherous trap into which a physician can fall and how a doctor must constantly maintain a high index of suspicion. I cannot for the life of me explain my blindness to the situation.

Donna is at this time five years sober, not depressed, and virtually free of anxiety. After the diagnosis of alcoholism was made, she entered a rehabilitation program and then became actively involved in AA. She is alive and well, not because of my treatment, but in spite of it.

These lines are being written during an intermittent stop in an airplane flight. We are delayed on the ground, having been informed that we lack a copilot and that a replacement will not arrive for an hour.

I have a high index of suspicion. I have treated several airline pilots for alcoholism, and I know the problem to exist even in this position of utmost sensitivity where many human lives are dependent on quick thinking and intact reflexes. The pilots whom I have treated have assured me that there are more where they come from and that the problem continues to be concealed far too long before submission to treatment is demanded.

I choose to suspect that the delay on this flight is caused by someone's lethal benevolence and, in my present frustration, this is obviously not benevolent to me or my one hundred copassengers. But if I am correct, it is of least benevolence to the errant copilot.

Benevolence Lethal to the Family

Up to this point, we have been discussing the harmful effects *on the alcoholic* of some well-intended but erroneous maneuvers by those in the alcoholic's environment. We should also be aware, however, that many of those maneuvers are also destructive to the *nonalcoholic family members* themselves.

The wife who tries to control the alcoholic husband's drinking, or compensate for it or conceal it, is apt to drive herself to ruin. First, she can collapse from sheer exhaustion. Her ingenious efforts to keep her husband away from alcohol, or alcohol away from her husband, will always be surpassed by the greater ingenuity of the alcoholic. Second, attempting to compensate for the misdeeds of the alcoholic is like trying to fill a bottomless pit: exhaustive efforts with no satisfactory results. Third, lying is a degenerating behavior, and lying to cover up a spouse's drinking is no exception. The endless efforts expended on these futile maneuvers take their toll on the nonalcoholic spouse, and we soon have two sick parents.

The children of the alcoholic, who could have had at least one healthy parent, now have none.

Obviously, children who have lived in the chaotic home of an alcoholic parent are vulnerable to problems of their own. It is interesting to note that children sometimes have more anger and resentment toward the nonalcoholic parent than toward the alcoholic. It seems that some children have an intuitive feeling that the drinking is an illness for which the alcoholic parent is not completely at fault. They may sense that their father does indeed love them, and this feeling is reinforced by his manifestation of love during his sober periods. But whereas they can forgive their father, they may feel greater anger at their mother.

The children stated that their mother had become so wrapped up with their father's drinking that she had no time to devote to them. They seemed to be aware that nothing that she was doing made any difference in his drinking, so why was she so preoccupied with worthless actions which deprived them of the care and attention they needed? The mother always seemed to be wallowing in self-pity about how cruel the father had been to her, and she seemed to expect the children to somehow compensate for her being shortchanged in life. At times she appeared to make them the recipients of all the anger and hostility she felt toward the father but was afraid to express. At other times she was overindulgent, as if trying to make up to them for giving them a drinking father. At times she seemed to hold on to her children for dear life, seeking in them the security she lacked in her husband. At other times she manifested an attitude of mastery and self-sufficiency, since she was in charge of the family. These children would indicate that at least they could account for their father's mood vacillations, since he was under the effects of alcohol, but the mother was a total enigma.

Probably the greatest single obligation of a parent,

beyond providing the essential physical and material needs of the child, is to prepare him for the world of reality in which he must live as an adult. The real world is one that expects mature behavior from an adult, which is essentially being responsible for one's actions. When the nonalcoholic spouse protects the drinker from suffering the consequences of his actions, the message conveyed to the child is that one need *not* necessarily be responsible for one's behavior. Regardless of what the parent may preach to the contrary, the principle that actions speak much louder than words holds true. Perhaps this is one reason why children of alcoholics are more likely to become alcoholic themselves.

When the mother is the drinker, the husband, in an attempt to shield the wife, may try to keep the home functioning as close to normal as possible by assigning the household duties to the oldest child. I have seen children of eleven and twelve who were expected to prepare the meals, compile the grocery list, and clean the house while their mother was lying in bed drunk. These children, who were being deprived of both the time needed for their studies and the fun of childhood, developed a hatred of both parents: the mother for being drunk and the father for placing the burden of the home on them.

Children who are verbally taught not to lie, but who observe the sober parent lying to cover up for the drinker, have to be confused, and they may develop serious defects in morality. Furthermore, if the parent whom they conceptualize as the authority figure has an illness that alters his behavior, their respect for authority is not as profoundly affected as when the drinking parent is considered to be a morally deficient person. And if the drinking parent is indeed sick, why is the sober parent perpetuating the illness by shielding him or her from the consequences of drinking?

There is help available for children of an alcoholic

family, but sometimes the nonalcoholic parent will not permit the child to receive counseling lest it expose the secret he or she is guarding. Or the wife may be frightened of her husband's reaction if he were to discover that the child went for counseling. Such "considerate" endeavors purportedly in the interest of the alcoholic are clearly detrimental to the child.

Children too can develop the feeling that they are responsible to a greater or lesser degree for the alcoholic's drinking. "Get those damn kids out of my hair," the drinker may holler. "They are driving me out of my mind." Or the well-intending mother may say, "Don't talk to Daddy now. You might upset him." Children tend to believe the parent and feel guilty for contributing to or causing the drinking.

The child of an alcoholic parent should be introduced to Al-Ateen groups, if they are available, where he can discover that his dilemma is not unique, that the parent's drinking is an illness, that the drinker's abusive behavior is the manifestation of a disease and not a rejection of him nor an expression of lack of love. He can discover that in no way is he the cause of the drinking. And at a tender age, he can learn how constructive interreliance among people can operate.

In conjunction with Al-Ateen, or in communities where Al-Ateen is not available, counseling can be most helpful. The nonalcoholic parent is too deeply involved in the problem to serve as counselor for the child. Parents should not see counseling as an indication of their inadequacy as parents, any more than taking a child to the pediatrician when this is necessary. After all, if sober and purportedly healthy parents cannot ask for help for themselves or the children, how can they expect the sick alcoholic to do so for himself?

16

Allowing the Confrontation

From what has been said, it is evident that regardless of what may have initiated an individual's addiction to or abuse of alcohol or drugs, the persistence of the behavior over the long term is generally possible only in a fertile environment, that is, one that protects the drinker or addict from having to face the consequences of his behavior. A change in the environment to remove protective maneuvers will thus allow the confrontation with consequences to occur.

There is good reason why groups such as Alcoholics Anonymous and Al-Anon have chosen the serenity prayer for the opening of their meetings: "God grant me the serenity to accept that which I cannot change, the courage to change that which I can, and the wisdom to know the difference." As a guide for human conduct this prayer has broad application in every phase of life. The AA people were fortunate in recognizing the value of this rule and adopting it as a guide for living.

In spite of its beautiful simplicity, a word of elucidation is appropriate. It is important to realize just what it is that cannot be changed and must be accepted as a given fact of life. Trying to change the unchangeable is obviously an act of futility, and it is not only a waste of energy but also results in the hostility, frustration, anger, and bitterness consequent to failure. On the other hand, resigning oneself unnecessarily to circumstances that can be favorably altered is tragic, since one suffers unnecessarily. The crucial element is the third ingredient, namely, to have the wisdom to recognize which is which.

A safe rule of thumb is that the unchangeables are other people, and the changeable is oneself. If this guide were adhered to, people would direct their efforts toward changing their own personality and behavior, rather than expecting others to change to suit them. Unfortunately, the reverse is generally true. Most people accept themselves as givens, *their* attitudes are correct, *their* opinions are sound, *their* way of dealing with things is just and appropriate. Some do not even entertain the slightest element of doubt that things might not be as they perceive them. They therefore dedicate all their energies to bringing others around to their way of thinking and acting. Of course, the others involved generally have a similar position. We then have two opposing forces, each trying to produce change in the other, and both becoming disillusioned, frustrated, and exhausted. The tragedy is that these feelings lead to a great deal of misery, which generally serves to entrench one's self-righteous position, projection of all the fault onto the other, and demands of even more change. A vicious cycle of futility and misery is thus generated.

To accept that which we cannot change: Untreated alcoholism is virtually always progressive, leading to consequences of which death is not the most severe. Tragic as death may be, it is at least over and done with. The dead person suffers no longer; the family readjusts to the loss and can rebuild itself. Ongoing alcoholism may be worse than death to the family, and the results of brain deterioration may condemn the drinker to a sub-human type of existence, undoubtedly more painful than death.

The course of unchecked alcoholism is predictable and relentless. The only variable is time. Some drinkers may go along for decades before alcohol takes its gruesome toll, whereas others may have a fulminating course, with serious mental and physical damage developing in only a few years.

Of course one can find a rare exception to the rule, a case in which a person stopped drinking permanently without outside help. There are also cases of lobar pneumonia that have survived without antibiotics, and even cases of proven cancer that have survived for many years without treatment. Yet, no one in his right mind would neglect antibiotic therapy in the hope that he might be one of the small minority that survives. Similarly, it is foolish to expect alcoholism to be arrested without treatment. Our hopes and wishes notwithstanding, the alcoholic will progress to a bitter end unless he receives effective treatment.

Case 28

A thirty-six-year-old woman consulted me because of her husband's destructive drinking. Her husband was forty-four years old and had a successful law practice. In spite of his drinking, he had never missed a single day at the office. However, the home situation was unbearable. She and the three children were being subjected to indescribable torture. She had begged her husband to get help, but he had persistently refused, denying the existence of a problem. She had left him on three occasions, returning only after he had solemnly promised he would stop drinking; but the periods of abstinence never lasted longer than a week. "He is driving us all crazy but just refuses to recognize it. I swear to you, Doctor, I cannot take one more day of this hell. Not one single day more," she wept.

I told the woman that she had clearly reached the solution to her dilemma. She looked at me with a puzzled expression. "It is obvious," I said. "Your husband has made it abundantly clear that he does not intend to stop drinking. You have made it clear that you cannot possibly endure any more of his drinking. Obviously, you must then be considering taking the children and leaving."

The woman looked at me with bewilderment. "Leave him? How could I do that!"

"Quite simply," I said. "If you should decide to leave him, then you find a place to live and move there. If you don't have adequate resources of your own, you can see whether your family can help you out until you get a job. Perhaps you might temporarily have to get on welfare. But if what you say is true, that you cannot take one more day of abuse, and since he shows no intention of changing, then your course is decided."

"But I couldn't leave him," she protested. "How will he get to work? I have to drive him to the office three or four times a week because he is in no shape to drive."

I told the woman that driving her husband to work was essentially encouraging his drinking, and that she had to decide either to just put up with the behavior she is condemning or to let him take the consequences thereof.

"But how can I leave him?" she said. "What would happen if he drove the car into a tree?"

> "Then," I said, "you would be a charming young widow of thirty-six. If, however, you continue to condone his drinking and protect him from drunken driving, he will eventually succumb to cirrhosis and die from liver failure. But that may be a long time coming, and may not occur for sixteen years, at which time you will be an older widow of fifty-two. You do not have the choice whether he will die from alcohol, only perhaps how and when he will die. You do not have the choice as to whether you will be a widow, but only whether you will be widowed when you are young enough to make a new start in life or whether you will be much older and far less capable of having a new life."

My response to the woman may be criticized as callous, but I assure you that I empathized with her. Unable to see the reality and carrying the empty hope that there was something she or anyone else could do to alter her husband's behavior, she had to be confronted with the facts.

This woman's denial of reality was no less than her husband's. Six months after the conference, I received a request from the hospital switchboard operator one night to return an emergency call. It was the attorney's wife, informing me that he had been arrested for drunken driving and was to appear at traffic court that night. Should she go to the hearing?

"Absolutely not," I told her. "You were not arrested for drunken driving. He was. You stay home and go to sleep."

Several hours later, I was awakened by another urgent call. It was this woman, who was at traffic court. Her husband was too intoxicated to appear at the hearing and should she try to get him to the hospital? Again, I advised her to go home and let him deal with his predicament. The very next day, I learned that she had taken him to a hospital from which he had signed himself out less than twelve hours following admission.

Experience with treatment of alcoholics has made this much evident: The alcoholic will change when he is ready, and not one minute earlier. Postponing that moment of readiness is to no one's advantage.

Yet the woman's argument cannot be brushed aside lightly. She is claiming that if she leaves the alcoholic husband or discontinues what is essentially her enabling behavior, he might kill himself as a result of the drinking. This problem presents itself in a variety of different forms. Not infrequently the alcoholic threatens suicide if the spouse leaves, and such threats cannot be dismissed as empty. There is no truth to the colloquialism that those who threaten suicide do not carry through with it. It is also possible that left to his own resources, the drinker may suffer from malnourishment and sustain severe injury or rapid physical deterioration.

Parents of alcoholic children may feel that if they detach themselves, the child may progress from alcohol to drugs, commit a crime to support the habit, or turn to prostitution. In any case, producing the crisis is fraught with real danger.

The point to remember is that if a crisis is precipitated, things can go one of two ways. The alcoholic may finally be confronted with the consequences of his drinking, and may even suffer physical deterioration, loss of job, and the like. However, these consequences may break through the barrier of denial and rationalization, and he may then recognize his illness and seek help for himself. It is also distinctly possible that with the props pulled out, he may destroy himself, whether by intentional or unintentional suicide. Perhaps the chances are fifty–fifty, and that is a formidable risk.

However, although producing a crisis may carry a 50 percent mortality, *not producing the crisis generally carries a 100 percent mortality.* Again, the course of untreated alcoholism is usually relentless. Disaster can only be postponed, not avoided, and any apparent gains in postponing the disaster have to be carefully evaluated. The ravages of the alcoholic's behavior on the family may be too high a price to pay if all that is to be gained is postponement of the inevitable.

Family members who can be helped to recognize this fact and are willing to eliminate enabling behavior should be fully informed of the possibilities subsequent to a crisis. They should not be urged to precipitate a crisis until they are fully aware of its possible consequences and appear ready to deal with them. Even after sufficient counseling has been provided to help them make an appropriate decision, a great deal of support is necessary to help them maintain that decision and live with its consequences.

If the woman stops driving her husband to work, and should he indeed have a fatal accident, she is apt to feel guilty and responsible for his death. At that point, the guilt may be so intense that all the memories of the many years of suffering fade, and she is left with a profound depression. The only way to avoid this result is with adequate preparation before the precipitation of crisis and ongoing support and counseling after the decision has been implemented. If the crisis should not have a favorable result, more intensive support is essential.

The nonalcoholic family member should ideally have multiple resources in reaching a decision, and these should operate in functional harmony. If the wife, for example, receives concurring opinions from the physician, pastoral counselor, and alcoholism therapist, and if they are in some communication with each other to provide a unified approach, her task and burden are made much easier.

Group therapy is of inestimable value in such situations. The family member or members have an opportunity to unburden themselves and clarify their feelings as they explain them to others, in addition to receiving valuable counseling. Often they are put in touch with some of their more profound feelings, of which they may have been unaware.

The Al-Anon fellowship cannot be equaled in its constructively supportive role. Made up of graduates of the universities of experience, Al-Anon can provide the quality of practical wisdom which cannot be found in books on psychology and sociology.

The most common obstacle to acceptance of Al-Anon by newcomers is their disillusionment when they discover that Al-Anon cannot provide the desperately sought instruction on how to stop the alcoholic from drinking. The neophyte understandably seeks help particularly from those whose spouses have recovered, asking, "How did you do it? What do I have to do?" They may be disillusioned by the answers: "There is nothing you can do about your spouse. We can only help you do something about yourself." This reply is generally met with the objection, "But there is nothing wrong with me! He is the problem. If only the drinking were eliminated, our family could be happy." The people in Al-Anon may only reiterate that they have found out the hard way that there is nothing that can be done to change the alcoholic; furthermore it is simply not true that if only the drinking ceased everything would be all right. This is an illusion which persists because the drinking is generally so disruptive that it is only natural to project every discontent in the home onto it.

One woman confided to me that she had lived through fifteen years of absolute hell. They had a large family, and with the advent of each child the husband's drinking and abusive behavior increased in intensity. "For fifteen years I prayed for a miracle to happen. Four years ago, the miracle happened, my husband joined AA and has been sober since. We have a happy home now, but I must admit that during that first year of sobriety, as hard as I had prayed for those fifteen years that he would stop drinking, that's how hard I prayed that he would start again."

To the suffering spouse of the active drinker, this statement may appear to be crazy. Some spouses of recovering alcoholics, however, may well recall the enormous difficulties in the adjustment period, which may be so agonizing that drinking may actually seem to be the lesser of the evils. There are many reasons for this phenomenon, some of which are related to those poorly understood, perhaps unconscious and irrational, "needs" for having an active drinker in the family. But high on the list is the scapegoat factor. During the turmoil of the active drinking phase, all the family's ills—social, economic, sexual, parental—are attributed to the drinking. When it is discontinued and the other problems persist, the family is caught off guard and may be forced to acknowledge many other intrapersonal and interpersonal difficulties. The nondrinking spouse and children may now have to recognize some of their own problems or deficiences, which had heretofore gone unnoticed because of the readily available projection onto the drunkenness.

It is difficult to change one's own life-style and deeply engrained habits. There is considerable internal resistance to accepting that what one has always assumed to be correct may indeed not be so. Habits of personal attitudes and reactions may be even more resistant to change than behavioral habits, such as smoking and overeating, and heaven knows these are obstinate enough. Such change is even more difficult to accomplish when it seems so unnecessary. "Why should *I* change? *He's* the sick one with his crazy drinking."

Not infrequently, the wife of an alcoholic will consult me because the husband's drinking has persisted. "He went to two AA meetings and then refused to go to any more. He said he wasn't as bad as some of the stories he heard there. He says he has nothing in common with them and that after the meetings he had an even greater urge to drink." I then inquire about the wife's attendance at Al-Anon. "I went to two meetings, but I didn't get anything out of them. Maybe they're helpful to someone else, but not for me."

It is truly amazing how the wife is unaware that in this case she is exhibiting the same behavior that she is criticizing in her husband. Both tried a few meetings and both discontinued, probably for identical reasons. Alcoholics Anonymous demanded that the husband make some significant changes in *him*self, and Al-Anon advocated that the wife make some changes in *her*self. Neither cherished the idea of undergoing the discomfort which personal change requires.

There is yet another objection raised by some Al-Anon dropouts, "Why, I met a woman there who has been going for six months and her husband is still drinking. Why should I go if it is not going to help?"

If the woman had talked with the six-month veteran, she would have discovered her reason for attending Al-Anon. Her life has become more manageable. She no longer wastes her energy on futile tactics. She no longer rides the exhausting emotional rollercoaster of built-up hopes and disappointments. She no longer lives in fear that something she might do will trigger another drinking episode. She has come to realize that she cannot cause the drinking, nor can she stop the drinking. But very obviously inherent in the woman's criticism is the expectation that Al-Anon should bring about the sought-after change in the drinker rather than personality growth in the nonalcoholic family member. I can only repeat the omniscient remark made by an Al-Anon husband to the newcomer wife of a very heavy drinker, who kept on pressing the group for what she should do about her husband's terrible drinking. "Lady," the man said, "please understand that your husband does *not have* a drinking problem. *You* have the drinking problem. *He* has the drinking *solution*."

No truer words could be uttered. The one who is in pain is the one who should seek help. As long as the drinker anesthetizes himself with alcohol, he cannot feel the pain of his maladjustment. If the wife does feel the pain, she should accept help for herself. If circumstances change so that the consequences of the drinking break through the alcoholic anesthesia, the alcoholic may then become aware that he needs help. Such realization generally requires elimination of the "benevolent" maneuvers alluded to earlier.

Whether the family member goes for help to Al-Anon, a psychologist, psychiatrist, or other counselor, and regardless of what the alcoholic does or does not do about the drinking, there is another point to be remembered.

Case 29

A social work intern who had been in our alcoholism clinic for several months complained that he was totally frustrated with his work and did not think he would continue in his capacity. The specific incident that had provoked his frustration was the third relapse after intervals of several weeks' sobriety of an alcoholic with whom he had worked for four months. He had counseled the alcoholic twice a week and had met once weekly with both husband and wife, and in spite of this the man was drinking again.

I reminded the student of our discussion of the genesis of alcoholism and that regardless of what the underlying sources of stress might be, the alcoholic turned to alcohol because he was searching for immediate relief, which alcohol provided in a manner of minutes. Generally, even if the alcoholic could be assured of an eventual solution to his stress, he would be unable to withstand the waiting period if that were a matter of weeks or months (sometimes even days or hours). The hallmark of many alcoholics is a very low frustration tolerance and a demand for immediate results.

"Now tell me," I asked, "How long has this man been drinking?"

The student consulted his notes. "Twenty-one years," he replied.

"And you are frustrated because you have been unable to reverse a pattern of twenty-one years in four months. It seems that what you are looking for is immediate results. But I thought that this is precisely what we had defined as the pathology of the alcoholic. Now if you have fundamentally the same problem he does, how do you expect to help him?"

To say that an alcoholic's behavior is exasperating is a gross understatement. Yet, the expectation of total reversal or a dramatic change from the initiation of some kind of help or therapy is unrealistic. Change is slow and fraught with many disappointments on the way.

For the alcoholic who is willing to try AA or the family member interested in Al-Anon, I advise, "Attend twenty-eight meetings in twenty-eight days before even considering its value for you." Some people object to meetings because they don't enjoy them or because they interfere with their schedule. Rejection of AA or Al-Anon on these grounds is as foolish as rejecting an effective treatment for cancer because one doesn't enjoy it or one is too busy with other commitments. AA and Al-Anon are treatments for a life-threatening and sanity-jeopardizing condition. One takes treatment because one needs it, not because it is enjoyable. Almost invariably, people who accept either program do get to enjoy it immensely, but that is not the prime reason for which these programs should be sought.

In the production of crisis, there may be resistance factors over and above the psychological ones cited earlier. As difficult as living with an active drinker may be, the prospect of losing one's economic support is formidable. A wife with several children may have legitimate reason to feel insecure if she leaves her husband or does not help get him to work or does not call in to report his "upset stomach." The misery sustained from the drinking, bad as it may be, is at least a known entity. Living without a source of income is frightening, bewildering, and generally unspecified. Uncertainty is so threatening that the greatest suffering may be tolerated if it is a known quantity. An evil of far lesser character and intensity may appear much greater if it is unknown, whereas one's present problems may at least have the mitigation of familiarity.

Nothing can be as much help in dealing constructively with this dilemma as the support, combined experience, and practical wisdom of thousands of people who have traveled this path, having gone down both forks in the road. Here the empathy and constant availability of people in Al-Anon have no equal.

17

Understanding Alcoholism

I do not wish to violate the earlier recommendation I espoused, that is, not to tell anyone what specific steps to take in any given situation. The role of any therapist or counselor working with the nonalcoholic in the alcoholic's environment is to be an objective observer who can point out realities, which the involved person may be unable to see, and to help him avoid those faulty judgments that may arise from unwholesome pressures or motivations, some of which he himself may be unaware. Any suggestions offered here that seem to be specific instructions should be taken as generalizations and not as rigid guidelines.

First and foremost, anyone relating to an alcoholic in any significant manner, whether family member, physician, pastoral counselor, therapist, or employer, should become better informed about alcoholism. There are many misconceptions or myths, which can be dangerously misleading. True, there are some differences of opinion about certain aspects of alcoholism even among recognized authorities, and in such situations one must weigh opinions and come to one's own decision, but such a decision will be an enlightened one and not one arising out of ignorance.

There are basic books and articles on alcoholism, some of which are listed in the bibliography at the end of this book. Numerous seminars on alcoholism are available in larger communities. Finally, the open meetings of AA and Al-Anon family groups offer a wealth of data to the interested learner. These last resources have been grossly underutilized, and valuable as book learning may be, it cannot compare with the wisdom of experience. The medieval physician, Paracelsus, may have been too radical when he threw all the authoritative medical texts into a bonfire and told his students to learn medicine by observing patients, but his point is nevertheless well taken. Learning from books can convey some factual data, whereas sharing experiences with experienced people can provide a more profound and comprehensive grasp of the various parameters of alcoholism.

Alcoholics Anonymous refers to alcohol as "baffling, cunning, and powerful." This is an excellent description and should alert us to our most devious adversary. Trying to cope with or treat alcohol by means of sound logical approaches is apt to be disappointing and frustrating. Alcohol has a "logic" all its own, which has to be learned even if it cannot be understood. It often appears that the alcoholic himself is a victim of this logic rather than its master. Just about when one feels he has figured it all out and knows what to expect, the alcoholic will come up with a completely unanticipated maneuver that can set everyone's head spinning.

In working or associating with patients who are seriously ill mentally, one encounters delusions and thought processes that are grossly abnormal and can be recognized as such. The alcoholic, however, can be so thoroughly convincing in his reasoning that both he and those about him are taken in. The seductive and cunning character of alcohol can be fully appreciated only by observing it in operation and by associating with recovering alcoholics who can convey their own experiences.

Just what is meant when we say alcoholism is a disease? Is it a physiological disease wherein certain changes in body tissues or chemistry in the alcoholic are different from those in the nonalcoholic drinker? Is it a psychological disease similar to other types of mental illness, which are generally considered illnesses although no chemical or tissue change can be demonstrated? Or is it a combination of both of these?

The orthodox position on the disease concept of alcoholism is contained in the monograph by Jellinek (see the Bibliography). More recently, the role of genetic transmission has come under investigation, but reliable conclusions are elusive because of the difficulty in separating genetic from environmental factors. In the final analysis, barring a major breakthough in genetic manipulation, this issue is academic and does not really affect treatment.

New techniques and highly sensitive laboratory instruments have resulted in the discovery of some of the chemical substances in the brain which convey messages among the billions of brain cells. There is reason to believe that in the alcoholic there is an abnormality of these neurotransmitters. How and why this abnormality develops is not clear as yet; and why this abnormality develops in some people but not in others is also a mystery.

Is it possible that research will someday lead to discovery of a wonder drug that will correct neurophysiological abnormalities and permit the alcoholic to drink "safely" again? Is it possible that a method will be devised to identify those persons who are apt to become alcoholic, and that a kind of "inoculation" will be available to forestall this process? In a world replete with scientific wonders, nothing is impossible; but reality-oriented people must live in the here and now, and at this particular point in human history, these breakthroughs have not as yet occurred.

As of today, this much is clear: There is something different and abnormal about the use and reaction of the alcoholic to alcohol which distinguishes him from the nonalcoholic. It is further clear that the alcoholic does not want this distinction and very much desires to be like the nonalcoholic. There is nothing the alcoholic would like more than to be able to have a drink or two before dinner, a few drinks at a party or festive occasion, or a cold beer on a hot summer day. However, repeated efforts at social or controlled drinking have invariably proven disastrous. Alcohol seems to bring out behavioral reactions in him which do not occur in the nonalcoholic drinker, and he sooner or later loses control of the amount of alcohol consumed. He may develop a craving or a compulsive drive to drink which he appears unable to resist on his own.

This compulsion has been compared with those occurring in the obsessive-compulsive neurotic, who may feel intense anxiety unless he performs certain procedures or rituals which he knows to be nonsensical. These can be annoying and exhausting, yet all the logic and reasoning cannot deter the obsessive-compulsive neurotic from giving in to the compulsive drives. The alcoholic's unusual reactions to alcohol have also been compared to food allergies, where some people for no apparent detectable reason have distressing reactions to certain foods, which others tolerate without any difficulty whatever. The obsessive-compulsive neurotic does not wish to be that way, and the allergic individual would love to be free of his sensitivities. So would the alcoholic, who desires neither the compulsive drive nor the abnormal behavioral reaction.

Few alcoholics are true alcoholics from their first drink on. The overwhelming majority appear to have used alcohol safely for at least a time, which may vary from a few to many years, before they developed the dependence and loss of control. Is the alcoholic then responsible for the development of his condition?

Unless one adheres to a strict fundamentalist position which prohibits any use of alcohol at all, it is difficult to condemn the alcoholic for permitting the condition to develop. In western civilization, the use of alcohol is taken for granted and openly encouraged. Hardly anyone would think of having a festive affair without offering alcohol in abundance. Banquets and meetings are routinely ushered in by a cocktail hour, guests for dinner generally are served alcohol, and sales and business deals are often negotiated over a drink. Stopping off after a demanding day's work for a drink has become part of our work culture. In fact, anyone who departs from any of the accepted cultural uses of alcohol may sometimes be looked upon as being in some way deviant and abnormal, although there are valid statistics that indicate about 30 percent of the U.S. population does not use any alcohol at all.

Since one cannot therefore be blamed for the initial use of alcohol, it is difficult to condemn one for permitting progression of drinking to frankly pathological proportions. The process is generally so gradual and insidious that it escapes detection by anyone. Even the wife of the well-established alcoholic cannot usually point with any degree of precision to when the drinking pattern switched from normal to pathological. She may recall the first fight precipitated by alcohol or some other dramatic event, but it is evident that the dividing line between pathological and normal drinking had been crossed long before its occurrence. Perhaps there is no such line but rather a broad zone wherein there are degrees of progression imperceptible at the time they happen.

It thus appears that the alcoholic cannot be condemned for his initial use of alcohol, which is socially approved, nor for not detecting the gradual changes which lead to the full-blown alcoholism syndrome. By the time he has reached this stage, he is indeed a victim of whatever psychological and/or physiological alterations have occurred in his system to wrest from him the control of the nonalcoholic drinker and have imposed on him a compulsive drive of extreme intensity. At this point, the psychological defenses of denial and rationalization are fully operative to render him blind to the reality of his condition.

The unique feature about alcoholism is that full acceptance of the diagnosis is essentially the treatment of the condition. Whereas in other diseases, such as in diabetes, the acceptance of the diagnosis must be followed by appropriate treatment, as with insulin, in alcoholism the acceptance of the diagnosis *is* the treatment. From what has been said earlier, this fact can be understood. The principal pathology in alcoholism is primarily the delusion of being able to control alcohol. The alcoholic who "slips" after a period of sobriety usually has had a recurrence of the delusion of control, and subsequently will say, "I just thought I could get away with it." The first step in AA is recognizing that one is powerless over alcohol, and most of the rest of the steps are essentially to enable sincere acceptance of the first step.

One might challenge this fact by pointing to numerous people who assert that they are alcoholic but continue to drink anyway. This phenomenon can occur for one of two reasons. Sometimes a person simply does not care what happens to him. Life has become so meaningless that deteriorating or dying from alcohol not only is not a deterrent, but also may actually be consciously sought. In other instances, the affirmation that one is alcoholic is a superficial, intellectual acceptance, which does not really register emotionally. At the "gut" level, the denial remains intact. Such intellectual acceptance of one's alcoholism, known in the trade as *compliance* in contrast to *surrender*, is not the kind of acceptance that constitutes the essence of recovery.

Case 30

Elaine was in her second year of sobriety. She was active in AA, attending regularly and "leading." However, her sponsor had misgivings, although he could not pinpoint the problem.

One day Elaine called me on the phone and we discussed some problem that had arisen in the family. Almost abruptly she said, "Well, I'd better hang up now. I'm keeping you too long and you have more important things to do."

"What kind of 'more important things'?" I asked.

"Well, you have to take care of your patients," she said.

"Of course," I agreed. "But since I don't do surgery or any other procedures, my caring for patients consists of my talking to them, which I am doing now by talking to you. Now why is it more important that I talk to someone else rather than to you?" I asked.

"Oh, you know what I mean," Elaine said.

"Not unless you tell me, I don't," I replied.

"Well, I think its just wonderful that you take your time to deal with people like us," she said.

"People like whom?" I inquired.

"Oh, you know what I mean," she said.

"Look, Elaine," I answered, "I really do not possess the mind-reading skills you may think I have. People like whom?"

"I think it's great that you can deal with us dregs of humanity," she answered.

In several subsequent sessions in the office we dealt with Elaine's distorted self-concept. As long as she considered herself to be a "dreg of humanity" because she was an alcoholic, she could not sincerely accept the fact that she *was* an alcoholic. Although two years sober, Elaine was in compliance, going along with the diagnosis of alcoholism but not being able to feel at the gut level that she was truly powerless over alcohol. It was only after this resistance was overcome and Elaine was able to realize that an alcoholic is as good and worthy a person as anyone else, but one who happens to be suffering from an illness, that Elaine's sobriety took on a much more satisfactory character, with much greater contentment.

When the alcoholic's family recognizes alcoholism as a disease, it makes it easier for the alcoholic to reach that conclusion also. Conversely, as long as the family considers alcoholism a bad habit, a moral degeneracy, or a lack of willpower, the alcoholic is apt to maintain a similar concept.

If one accepts that alcoholism is indeed a disease, several conclusions follow. First, it is easier to realize that one does not cause another person to develop an illness by one's behavior toward him; hence, the spouse ought not to feel that he or she is the "cause" of the drinking. A corollary is that changing one's behavior is not going to eliminate the disease. Furthermore, promises are obviously meaningless in a disease. How could you accept a person's promise that he would not cough again? Similarly, threats can be as worthless in stopping alcoholism as migraine headaches. Both conditions are illnesses which require appropriate treatment.

The fact that a person has an illness does not, however, excuse him from anything. If a person refuses treatment for an illness whose symptoms cause misery to the family, there is really no reason why the family must continue to suffer. If the sick person would avail himself of effective treatment, everyone might be well and happy. If he decides to retain his illness and reject treatment, there is really no moral obligation for everyone around him to undergo martyrdom. One can even feel sorry for a person who refuses treatment for his illness, but one does not have to take the consequences.

Case 31

Ruth, a mother of four children, developed pulmonary tuberculosis and was hospitalized for treatment. She had an active disease, which meant that she could infect those around her.

After treatment in the hospital, Ruth became noncontagious, but on return home she refused to continue the antituberculosis medication. In spite of efforts by physicians and mental health counselors, Ruth did not take her medication, although she always promised to do so. She again developed an active disease, and after one of her children became infected with tuberculosis, it was necessary to remove her children from her.

No one argues that tuberculosis is a disease, and one can feel legitimate sympathy for a person who is its victim. Yet, endangering others by refusal to accept proper treatment cannot be condoned. Much the same can be said for alcoholism. It is a disease for which there is treatment. Nothing less than effective treatment will work, and if one rejects treatment, there is no reason why the family and others affected by the symptoms of the disease must suffer.

When the recovering alcoholic loses sight of the fact that he has a *disease*, which is arrested but never cured, he reverts back to ideas of control and willpower and is then prone to relapse. Similarly, the family members of the alcoholic, even after accepting that alcoholism is a disease, may occasionally lose sight of this belief.

The behavior of the active drinker can be so provocative and obnoxious that it must elicit feelings of anger and hostility in those who are victimized. When the wife of the alcoholic is told that her husband is a sick man and has an illness, she may begin to feel guilty for having been enraged at him or acting cruelly toward a sick person. Family members would feel much less guilty if alcoholism were not a disease and the drinker could be viewed as a selfish, irresponsible, and inconsiderate brute. Since our psychological systems are apt to work in a manner to relieve us from unpleasant feelings, there is a tendency for the family to revert back to thinking of alcoholism as evil behavior. It is therefore important for the family to realize that their reactions toward the active alcoholic's obnoxious and irresponsible behavior were completely normal at that time, and that there is no reason to harbor any guilt for these reactions even though they now recognize that alcoholism is an illness.

It has been noted that in some instances where alcoholics recover by becoming involved in AA, there are conflicting feelings in the spouse. On the one hand, there is immense gratitude that something is working, but on the other hand, there is anger that the alcoholic did not stop drinking for the spouse's sake.

Case 32

Evelyn was forty-eight when she was brought to the hospital by her husband for help with alcoholism. He stated that he was at his wit's end. They had four children who were being wrecked by their mother's heavy drinking. The home had become intolerable: no meals prepared, no housework done, no clothes washed. When not out cold in a stupor, Evelyn walked around like a zombie. The usual pleas and threats by the husband and the children had been to no avail.

After detoxification, Evelyn became active in AA. Her husband was elated with her recovery, but after several months of sobriety he began manifesting undisguised disdain for AA. Although he never prevented her from going to meetings, he made no secret of his resentment of the organization.

In a discussion with the husband, it became obvious that he was bitter because his entreaties and the pleas of the children that she stop drinking had been futile, whereas associating with the people in AA had been effective. As he saw it, his wife had greater respect and consideration for those people than for him and the children and would do for them what she had not done for her family.

Evelyn's husband was helped to see that her drinking was an illness for which AA was the treatment. Just as recovering from pneumonia after treatment with penicillin does not mean that one has greater love or respect for penicillin than for one's family, so does recovery with AA not reflect on one's feelings for the family. Once the husband understood the nature of the disease and its treatment, the resistance to AA disappeared.

Understanding the natural course of the disease can prevent the family from falling into the trap of a false sense of security. It is not unusual for the husband to stop drinking after he becomes aware that his wife has gone for help. Perhaps he feels threatened that the counseling his wife will receive will endanger the marriage. He may stop drinking for a few weeks and tell the wife that since he is no longer drinking, there is no need for her to continue in counseling. The wife, thrilled with his abstinence and fearful of upsetting the applecart, is apt to discontinue her counseling, only to discover soon that her optimism was premature. Had she understood that alcoholism is an illness which will not disappear without treatment, she might not have let the brief period of abstinence deter her from getting help for herself.

Finally, the recognition that alcoholism is a disease will eliminate futile attempts at punishing the drinker for his behavior. Punishment will be no more effective in curbing alcoholism than it will in any other disease. Some authorities contend that the alcoholic, who is generally guilt-laden, feels even more guilty after a binge, and when he is punished, he feels he has atoned for his guilt and is now free to drink again. But when we say that punishment is futile, this does not mean that the alcoholism should be condoned. If the alcoholic refuses treatment for his illness, the family should obtain the necessary counseling and guidance on how to extricate themselves from the frustrations of the situation. The combination of counseling by a competent therapist and guidance by Al-Anon members is most valuable and productive.

Most experts in treatment of alcoholism maintain that "once an alcoholic, always an alcoholic," or as one recovering alcoholic put it figuratively, "once a cucumber becomes a pickle, it cannot go back to being a cucumber again." Their approach to treatment is total abstinence, not only from alcohol in any shape or form, but abstinence also from sedatives, potent pain killers, and most tranquilizers.

Yet there have been dissenting opinions; various cases seem to indicate that return to responsible drinking did occur. I believe that these must be scrutinized most carefully.

I do not doubt that some alcoholics returned to "controlled" drinking *for a period of time*. Not all relapse into immediate drunkenness after their first attempt at "social" drinking, but almost invariably this phase comes to a calamitous end. Sometimes the period of "control" is a few weeks' duration, sometimes even months.

Case 33

Ron was a forty-four-year-old inspector upon whose efficacy and reliability many lives depended. He was admitted to a rehabilitation center at the insistence of his employer, who found his drinking to be incompatible with the sensitive nature of his work.

During treatment, Ron never accepted that alcohol was forever forbidden to him. He was different. He was strong-willed and determined. He would show us that he could drink safely.

Two months after discharge, he called to inform me that he was abstaining during the week but that on Saturdays he consumed a six-pack of beer. He was attending one AA meeting a week, and both his wife and employer were pleased with him. I told him he was toying with disaster and that he should follow our instructions for total abstinence as well as significantly increase his AA involvement.

On the anniversary of his admission, Ron came to the office, triumphant with his performance: a full year of controlled drinking. It was still only a six-pack, once a week.

Five months later, I received a call from Ron's wife. There had been a change in Ron's drinking over the past two weeks, and the past four days he had been missing, his whereabouts unknown. He turned up in a motel in a nearby state, having spent four days in drunken oblivion. This time, the job was gone.

However, anyone who had observed Ron's progress at the end of sixteen months might have erroneously concluded that he had successfully returned to controlled drinking.

Perhaps isolated examples may be found of individuals who had met the criteria for true diagnosis of alcoholism and who returned to controlled drinking without relapse. I believe that each such case can probably be matched by a documented case of a person who fell from the fourth floor of a building and survived unharmed, or that of a driver emerging unscratched from a car that had been totally wrecked. Yet no person in his right mind would leap from the fourth floor or drive his car into a tree on the assumption that he will be the rare survivor.

In 1976, the highly publicized Rand report implied that return to controlled drinking might be feasible for some alcoholics. Four years later, the 1980 sequel indicated that persons who had become "alcohol dependent" rarely succeeded in returning to "safe" drinking. Given the many and far-reaching disastrous consequences of relapse, increasing this likelihood by condoning a return to controlled drinking is ill advised.

I have advised all my patients that their names and addresses are on file with me, and that if and when science develops a proven, safe method of social drinking, I will immediately inform them. Until then they should adhere to the simple but time-proven maxim, "If you don't take the first drink, you won't get drunk."

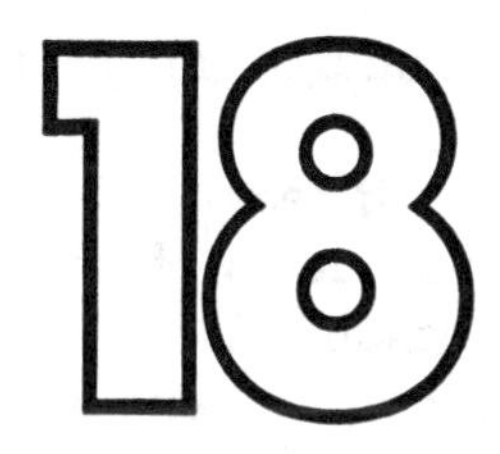

Ineffective Home Remedies

Almost invariably family members of an alcoholic will relate with exasperation the various techniques they have utilized to bring the problem under control and express their bewilderment that such apparently reasonable steps had proven to be so absolutely futile. Sometimes they will add, "There must be something more seriously wrong with him than just alcoholism. He must be mental!"

Some wives believe that leaving with the children for several weeks, and not returning until the husband has promised to mend his ways, should deter recurrent drinking. It is of interest that they may repeat this "remedy" several times, even after it has been demonstrated to be ineffective. They do not perceive that punishing the alcoholic does nothing to arrest the condition. Of course, there may also be the situation in which the husband considers the temporary absence of a nagging wife and noisy kids to be a welcome respite, and what she thinks is a punishment may actually be perceived by him as a reward.

Even if leaving is clearly painful for the alcoholic, the technique is of no value if its purpose is to "teach him a lesson." Alcoholism is an illness, and sick people can be helped only by appropriate treatment, not by being taught "lessons."

Screaming at the alcoholic, shaming him in front of the children, reciting a long list of harmful things he has done to the family, making him feel guilty, depriving him of sexual relations because he had gotten drunk—all these and many other punitive maneuvers are worthless. Hurting the alcoholic only adds fuel to the fire. *The alcoholic is a person who is already in severe pain.* Increasing his pain can hardly help.

Very few alcoholics drink heavily because they like the taste of alcohol, and some will admit that they actually hate the taste. I know of one alcoholic who had an obstruction of the esophagus which made it impossible for him to swallow anything, and he was saved from starvation by an operation that created an opening directly into his stomach through the abdominal wall; he would feed himself by introducing a liquid nutrient through a funnel directly into his stomach. Two days after discharge from the hospital he was returned, drunk, and to our surprise reported that he poured the whiskey via the funnel into his stomach. When we told him this was insane, he replied, "Hell no! It's the best way yet. You don't have to taste the damn stuff."

The alcoholic generally uses alcohol to provide some type of relief. Alcohol can be viewed as an anesthetic; it eliminates painful feelings. It is therefore safe to assume that the alcoholic generally drinks to kill his pain. Increasing his pain is certainly no way, then, to eliminate his use of the pain-killer.

Of course, the behavior of the alcoholic can be so irritating and repulsive that it arouses enormous anger in those about him, and when you are intensely angry at someone it is difficult to understand that he is a person who is badly hurt. Furthermore, there is a reflex to strike back at someone who is hurting you. However, it should be understood that punishing the alcoholic will do nothing to arrest the drinking and may even contribute to its progression.

There is an important distinction between punitive action against the alcoholic, which is worthless, and allowing him to face the natural consequences of his drinking, which can be most helpful. The former can become a kind of morbid game, the alcoholic perhaps trying to outfox everyone by surreptitious drinking or perceiving the punishment as atonement for his misbehavior—which has thus "wiped the slate clean" and permitted renewed drinking. On the other hand, not protecting the alcoholic from the consequences of his drinking simply makes his drinking unprofitable for him *of its own accord,* and it may lead to recognition of his condition.

The distinction may seem imperceptible, but there is actually a great difference between the wife who leaves the alcoholic husband in order to teach him a lesson and the wife who leaves because she has no intention of taking any more abuse. The former is acting punitively, and the message conveyed is "I'm going to punish you for being bad." As mentioned, this kind of action gets nowhere. The latter is saying, "Perhaps you are sick rather than bad. I am not threatening you, and I am not punishing you. I am only looking out for myself, and there is no reason why I should suffer from your illness for which you reject effective treatment." Similarly, denying sexual relations as a punishment is of no value, whereas indicating that one cannot be intimate with an intoxicated person is of positive value. The two may look alike but actually are vastly different.

In the process of treating the alcoholic we discover

how deeply this person has been hurt, and often, that he is exquisitely sensitive. The sensitivity is probably of pathological origin, but the alcoholic doesn't know this. All he knows or feels is his pain. He is often aware of the suffering he is inflicting upon his family, and nothing is more familiar than the self-effacement, self-torment, and self-castigation of the alcoholic in remorse. However, this guilt may cause a pain so intolerable that he now turns to alcohol to relieve this new pain, and we thus have a self-perpetuating vicious cycle.

Included in the therapy of the alcoholic is the reduction of the pathologic sensitivity, hence elimination of unhealthy perceptions of pain. The alcoholic is helped to attain a better self-image and an improved sense of self-esteem; the better he feels about himself, the less will be his need to drink. He is helped to recognize that brooding over what he has done to others is an exercise in futility, and that there are constructive ways of righting wrongs. The entire recovery program is directed toward getting the alcoholic to act and feel about himself in such a way that there will be no need for recourse to anesthetics.

19

For the Therapist

The problem presented by the alcoholic or the family member to the physician, psychiatrist, psychologist, social worker, or clergyman is not always that of excessive drinking. Alcohol may not even be mentioned in the presenting complaint, but if an alcohol problem is present, nothing that the therapist does is apt to be of much help until it is resolved. The high incidence and ubiquity of alcoholism necessitates that the counselor maintain a high index of suspicion that alcohol abuse may be involved. The reluctance to investigate the use of alcohol or pills for fear of insulting the patient or client indicates misunderstanding of alcoholism as a disease and is an example of lethal benevolence.

Marital infidelity often occurs against a background of excessive drinking. The alcoholic may find someone who is a drinking companion, in contrast to his wife, who nags him about his addiction. The wife may have tolerated the alcoholism for years, and when driven to seek help by her discovery of an extramarital affair, focuses only on the latter, which may actually be a consequence of the alcoholism.

Although there may be many reasons for debt, the complaint of persistent financial difficulty in the presence of an apparently adequate income should raise the suspicion of alcoholism, as should a pattern of frequent job changes, especially to jobs of lesser pay.

Alcoholism can produce a single-parent family, when the drinking spouse is away from home more than his work demands or when he is so disabled by drink that he cannot participate in the guidance and discipline of his children. The family may become isolated from the extended family or friends if the threat of excessive drinking and embarrassing behavior lead to avoidance of family gatherings or social events. Any of these complaints warrant investigation into drinking as a possible etiology.

The widespread toxic effects of alcohol on almost every system of the body should make alcoholism a consideration in every physician's differential diagnosis. In patients admitted for treatment of alcoholism, I have found people who have been taking anticonvulsant medication for years because of a diagnosis of idiopathic epilepsy, whereas the seizures were caused by alcohol or drug withdrawal. In such situations, the anticonvulsants are generally unnecessary if the abuse is arrested and of little help if it continues. Some patients are on blood-pressure medication, having been diagnosed as hypertensive, whereas the blood pressure may return to normal after a month or so of abstinence. Some patients have been taking medication to lower their blood-sugar levels, which may decrease very nicely once alcohol is eliminated. Patients with peptic ulcers or other digestive problems are medicated and prescribed special diets, whereas the greatest dietary offender, alcohol, is not eliminated. Others have been thought to have various other diseases or considered to be psychoneurotic; in reality they were suffering from the symptoms of alcoholic anemia or polyneuropathy. In all these situations, the patient rarely volunteers the correct data for alcohol consumption, and the physician fails to pursue this avenue aggressively.

Case 34

The Reverand A. is a fifty-seven-year-old minister whom I was asked to see on consultation because of a suspected psychosomatic condition. He had been hospitalized for a week because of complaints of severe pain and weakness affecting his right arm and left leg. Extensive X-ray and laboratory studies were all negative.

On interviewing the patient, I could not come up with any findings to warrant a psychiatric diagnosis. I then inquired about the use of alcohol or medications. He smilingly assured me that his position would hardly allow him to drink, and besides, he really did not like alcohol the few times he did use it. He denied regular use of any medication.

I found that there was slight enlargement of the liver, and that on the first two days in the hospital, the patient had been quite nervous and had been given tranquilizing medication during the day and a sedative at night. I then asked the nurse to call me when the patient's wife visited him.

I met with the wife away from the patient's room and advised her that thus far the diagnostic workup had revealed nothing to account for the pain and weakness, but that I wondered whether we had all the pertinent facts. I asked her if she could tell me about the patient's use of alcohol.

Mrs. A. became visibly uncomfortable and hesitating. She then asked me whether I would have to let her husband know what she told me. At that point, I already had my answer, but I told her that we could not play a game of having a person ask for our help while significant information was being withheld. I suggested that she not tell me anything that I was not free to communicate to the patient, and that perhaps she ought to have a serious talk with her husband about being truthful with the doctors if he expected their help.

Mrs. A. then told me that her husband had sworn her to secrecy about his drinking. For at least the past year, he was drinking about a pint of whiskey daily. He was able to time his drinking so that it had not interfered with his ministerial functions, and he had never become rowdy when intoxicated. He was a gentle drunk who went to sleep after drinking.

The correct diagnosis of alcoholic neuropathy could have been easily overlooked in this case. A physician might think that surely a person who comes for help with physical complaints will be truthful with the doctor in his quest of relief, but this simply does not apply to the alcoholic patient.

Once the diagnosis of alcoholism is made, I suggest to the therapist of any profession or calling not to assume complete and sole responsibility for treatment. The active drinker's behavior and propensity to get into complex difficulties any time of day or night are such that any therapist will quite soon become exhausted and frustrated; he not only will seek to extricate himself from this relationship but also is apt to swear off any future involvement with an alcoholic patient. The alcoholic's dependency even once abstinence is begun may manifest itself on vacations (patient's or therapist's), on weekends, or in the early hours of the morning. No one person can be all things to the alcoholic.

The therapist should identify his specific role. The physician can provide the detoxification and evaluation of physical complications and their treatment. The psychotherapist or counselor may provide vital insights and support in regularly scheduled sessions, but generally that is where his commitment should end. The patient should be advised that frequent attendance at AA meetings is mandatory. He may resist it for one or more reasons, but this resistance should not be permitted. It is my practice to tell patients that AA is my prescription, and that if they do not accept my prescription, there is no point in their coming to me and they are free to seek help elsewhere.

Alcoholics Anonymous is available everywhere and virtually at any time. There are AA meetings when the therapist is on vacation or within driving distance from the patient's vacation spot. I know there are therapists who treat patients without AA involvement. I believe this is heroic but, in some situations, may feed into the patient's pathology. The most common resistance to AA is caused by the patient's denial of alcoholism or his wish to retain his option to someday return to social drinking; he therefore shuns treatment that excludes such options.

Case 35

Bob is a forty-four-year-old attorney who called for an appointment, but stated that there were valid reasons why he could not come to my office. He offered to pay for a dinner appointment at any restaurant of my choice. I told him this was impossible, and he reluctantly came to the office.

Bob stated that he drank at home every night and that his wife had advised him that she was separating because she could not tolerate it. He never drank away from home, and no one knew or suspected that he drank excessively. After the interview, which left no doubt that Bob was indeed alcoholic, I advised him that he needed to become involved in AA. Bob stated that this was impossible because he was a very prominent attorney and his practice would be jeopardized if it were known that he was alcoholic. In fact, his reluctance to come to my office arose from his fear of being seen and suspected of alcoholism.

I advised Bob that there were many excellent attorneys in the community whose practices did not suffer because of their participation in AA. Bob responded that his case was different because he was politically active and identification as an alcoholic would paralyze his political aspirations. "Remember what happened to Eagleton," he said. (Senator Eagleton was dropped from the vice-presidential spot on the Democratic ticket with George McGovern in 1972 because of the discovery of his psychiatric treatment.) I then advised Bob that I would see him for two sessions only, during which I would try to convince him to join AA, but that if I was unsuccessful, there was no point in any further sessions with me. I also prescribed Antabuse (a medication that causes a violently repulsive physical reaction if one drinks within several days of taking it) because I saw no value in talking with someone whose brain function was altered by alcohol.

In the next session, Bob reported that he had attended a meeting of the bar association at which liquor flowed freely and that he had noted one attorney who turned over his glass when liquor was served. "I recall your saying that there were other attorneys who recovered from alcoholism, and if this one is one of them, I wouldn't mind talking with him. I have great admiration for him." He identified the particular attorney whom I knew well from frequent contact at AA meetings.

I never had any future psychotherapeutic interviews with Bob, who is now five years sober, in active practice, and whose political promotions were not in the least jeopardized by his active involvement in AA.

The therapist who counsels the family member should be aware that he or she may know little or nothing about alcoholism, and that even after listening to a description of advanced alcoholic behavior, may deny that that person is alcoholic. Many people have their own definition of what an alcoholic is, and they may not wish to classify the drinker as such. They are also apt to have conflicting feelings and may be ambivalent about treatment. They may feel guilty about their own feelings or behavior and quite likely believe that they are at fault or the cause for the drinking, as the alcoholic has undoubtedly told them many times. They may feel completely alone in their suffering, convinced that no one else has had this experience. They may be frightened about possible repercussions, particularly the wife who is afraid of what the husband might do if he finds out she has gone for help. Finally, they are people who have been greatly deprived and deeply hurt by the active drinker and whose self-esteem has plummeted to the depths.

Just as taking on sole responsibility for treatment of the alcoholic can be rapidly exhausting and counterproductive, so can taking on the sole counseling of the nonalcoholic family member. This person can be so overwhelmed with the multitude of problems regarding the home, finances, and children that he can exhaust the therapist's time and patience. Here too every effort should be made to have the family member involved with the Al-Anon family groups and Al-Ateen for the children.

Above all, the family member should be made to recognize alcoholism as a disease. This recognition can help avoid the exhaustive, fruitless, frustrating, and often self-defeating methods of relating to the alcoholic. With Al-Anon as a guiding support, the counseling of the therapist can be most productive.

20

Need for Counseling

One of the reasons a book cannot be used as a source of specific guidelines is because each case has its unique features and requires individualized attention. It is therefore highly recommended that the nonalcoholic family member seek out a competent counselor who is familiar with alcoholism to study the particular problems arising in that family and help reach correct solutions.

Take the case of the alcoholic husband whose income begins to suffer as a result of the drinking, and the family cannot meet its needs. Should the wife find a job to augment the family income?

It can be argued that her working will aggravate the situation. First, it may play directly into the alcoholic's need for dependency. Perhaps the only thing that kept him going was his sense of responsibility in providing for his family. With this need lessened, he may totally abandon himself to alcohol. Second, we have established that a low sense of self-esteem is generally involved in the development of alcoholism. Seeing himself as an inadequate provider is apt to further depress his already low self-esteem and lead to even more escapism into alcohol. On the other hand, when the children need shoes and the food bills must be paid, can the mother deprive herself and the children of necessities?

Dilemmas such as these occur frequently, and there is no one answer applicable to all cases. In some instances, it may be possible and advisable for the wife and children to separate and support themselves; in others, this may not be feasible. What is appropriate at one point in time may not be appropriate at another stage even for the same family. Only careful individual consideration with the help of a competent counselor offers the best likelihood of arriving at appropriate solutions.

Having extolled the great virtues and values of Al-Anon, I must caution against some pitfalls, Al-Anon members will be the first to tell you that they cannot provide counseling. However, they may be in a position to recommend a competent counselor. In discussing problems with members of Al-Anon you are apt to hear what steps some of them took in their own cases. It is well to bear in mind that what was good for one may not necessarily be good for another.

The great advantage of Al-Anon is that it can help the family member recognize alcoholism as a disease over which the family has no control and to stop the various futile measures or home remedies. Another advantage of Al-Anon is that it directs the family member's attention away from the alcoholic and toward the non-alcoholic himself, where corrective action can be profitable. Since the delusion that one can control the alcoholic is apt to recur frequently, with consequent resumption of exhausting and worthless tactics, regular participation in Al-Anon is essential. The support of the fellowship enables the family member to discontinue the fruitless efforts at changing the alcoholic. These goals are better achieved in Al-Anon than in counseling. Once these goals are reached and maintained, counseling can be effective in helping the family deal with specific issues.

21

The Rehabilitation Center

The theme of this book has been the roles of those in the environment of the alcoholic and how their behavior can affect perpetuation or interruption of the disease. Except by implication, nothing was said about actual treatment of the alcoholic. This is a subject in itself, and the reader is referred to the Bibliography for several of the texts on therapy.

In several places throughout this book, there were references to treatment of alcoholism in a rehabilitation facility. Many people are familar with the need for brief hospitalization for detoxification and treatment of any of the physical complications of alcoholism. There is a general understanding of what happens in individual outpatient therapy or counseling sessions. But just what is the role of a residential rehabilitation program?

In my early years of working with alcoholics, the treatment modalities at my disposal were the hospital detoxification service, the outpatient clinic, referral to Alcoholics Anonymous, and in some cases, the medication disulfuram (Antabuse®), which, if taken as prescribed, helps the patient to surrender temporarily his ability to drink.* It became evident, however, that many alcoholics postponed involvment in AA or resumed drinking before they had attended enough meetings to have an impact. Furthermore, after drying out they would often be confronted by a spouse whose repeated disappointments following previous brief episodes of abstinence had resulted in an understandable skepticism and even an expectation of "I wonder how soon before the drinking starts again"; such anticipation can actually encourage a relapse. Finally, in the brief detoxification period the patient had no opportunity even to begin to learn new coping skills, and when confronted with the first challenge would often fall back on the "magic elixir" which relieved all distress, albeit at a near-lethal cost.

These pitfalls can be minimized by therapy in a residential rehabilitation program. In such a facility, the alcoholic spends a variable period of time, usually four or more weeks after detoxification, where under supervised abstinence he can begin more genuinely to accept the diagnosis of alcoholism, with its implication that for whatever reason he and alcohol must part ways. Sharing an environment with many other patients engaged in recovering from alcohol addiction, the patient does not feel himself to be uniquely "bad" and can more readily recognize alcoholism as an illness that needs to be treated, rather than a moral weakness or character defect of which one must be ashamed.

Under the guidance of experienced counselors, both in individual and group therapy, the alcoholic can realize

*Antabuse® is a medication that interferes with the metabolism of alcohol in such a manner that if alcohol is consumed even up to ten days after the medication, a very revulsive physical reaction occurs. Alcoholics who recognize their inability to control alcohol and are concerned that they might yield to the impulse to drink may take the medication daily, and thereby erect a formidable barrier to impulsive drinking.

how much of his behavior involved unnecessary escapist techniques and how he had developed a pattern of fleeing from problems which were well within his capacity to overcome. He can be helped to discover rich personality resources within himself of which he was unaware and how to appropriately accept assistance from other people when a particular problem appears to be beyond his own abilities. He is helped to recognize the destructive role of pathological guilt and clinging to resentments, both of which so often result in the need for oblivion in alcohol.

In many rehabilitation centers, particularly those located near the patient's residence, there are programs involving family members and even employers in a comprehensive approach, so that all may understand the goals sought and the methods to be used in achieving them. During the rehabilitation course a more adequate assessment can be made of social, cultural, educational, and/or vocational problems which may be an integral part of the patient's alcoholism, and steps can be initiated to meet these needs.

Rehabilitation programs may vary somewhat in points of relative emphasis on one or another phase of the alcoholism spectrum, and some may employ special techniques, such as psychodrama, relaxation techniques, biofeedback, depth analysis, and behavior modification. The aim of the rehabilitation program is to bolster the alcoholic's self-esteem, inititate a sense of self-trust and realistic trust in others, and help the patient develop constructive adaptive techniques in place of the pathologic and destructive mechanisms to which he had been accustomed.

It is quite common that following detoxification, although fervently expressing his desire to remain sober, the alcoholic will reject the recommendation for a residential rehabilitation program. All kinds of objections are raised: "I don't have the money"; "I can't be away from the job for a month"; "My husband and children need me at home"; and so on. Experience has shown that these are invariably feeble excuses. If the patient had suffered a heart attack requiring lengthy hospitalization and major curtailment of activities, none of these objections would have been given any consideration. When this is pointed out to the patient, he is apt to concede but say, "A heart attack is different." Therein lies the root of the problem. If the patient were only aware that drinking is every bit as threatening to his health and even his life as heart disease, he would be on the way to recovery. It is the denial of the gravity of untreated alcoholism that is part and parcel of the alcoholic's pathology of overall denial, which permits him to reject the recommended treatment and provide these transparent rationalizations. Although one may not be able to coerce the patient, it should be made manifestly clear by all in his environment that they do not concur with this refusal of effective treatment.

Case 36

> The president of a large financial firm called to inquire what he should do about one of his senior employees, whose drinking had progressed to the point where he could no longer permit him to manage the large sums of money which his position entailed. After obtaining a description of the problem, I advised the president that treatment for Mr. B. would involve several days of detoxification in a hospital, followed by a month in a rehabilitation facility, followed by continued involvement in AA. The president agreed that if Mr. B. would recover, he would maintain him at his position, but that if he did not, he would have to dismiss him with an early retirement pension.

Later that day, Mr. B. was in my office, and after I outlined the treatment plan, he said, "I'll go into the hospital for a few days, but I cannot take off a month." I told Mr. B. that I could only recommend what I felt was advisable but of course could not force him to accept my recommendation.

"But if I don't go along with your plan, I'll be dismissed," Mr. B. agreed. "That option is yours," I replied. "But you have a retirement pension don't you?"

"Doctor, I can't retire now. I still have a child to put through college, and I can't do that on a pension. I still need that job for at least five more years," he said.

I advised Mr. B. that I could not alter my prescription for treatment to please him. *Very* reluctantly he accepted the rehabilitation program.

Five sober years after completing the rehabilitation program, I met Mr. B., who was still very much at his job. "You know, Doctor," he remarked, "I've been in AA for five years now, and I've had a chance to observe others like myself in the program. I think that if I had not been in rehab and had gone directly from detoxification into AA, I would have caught on to the program and made it *eventually.* However, I think I would have had four or five 'slips' on the way. In my situation, I couldn't afford any slips, because they would have cost me my job. What the rehabilitation program did for me was enable me to benefit effectively from AA without any slips."

Many rehabilitation alumni have made similar observations. Whereas no rehabilitation program can claim anywhere near 100 percent success, nor even that slips will be prevented, it is true that a good rehabilitation program prepares the patient for more effective utilization of therapy and AA, thus minimizing the chances of relapse. In a disease as devastating as alcoholism, any plan that significantly decreases the chances of relapse is invaluable. Some programs require a personal commitment for several months, with possible extension as the individual case may necessitate.

Whereas even a brief relapse after treatment is always regrettable, it should not be interpreted as a sign of therapeutic failure. Just as many people will not accept the veracity of a sign declaring "Wet Paint" and must test the newly painted surface themselves, so the alcoholic is prone to test whether what he was told in rehabilitation is true, namely, that he could not return to safe, controlled drinking again. The test is invariably failed, and the patient may then settle down to the business of staying sober.

It is important to realize that no matter how excellent a rehabilitation program may be, there is no way that one can consider himself "cured" after twenty-eight days, weeks, or even months. Rehabilitation is a catalyst in the recovery process, but additional counseling is often necessary for a variable period of time, and indefinite participation in AA is the rule for maintaining sobriety. Again, enlightened involvement of the significant others in Al-Anon and/or counseling can facilitate the resumption of a constructive, alcohol- or chemical-free adjustment to life.

22

Living with Sobriety

One of the greatest shocks the family of the recovering alcoholic may undergo is the realization that sobriety does not solve all its problems. For so long, the focus has been on the drinking and ensuing behavior that the spouse understandably sees alcohol as responsible for all the misery, expecting that when the drinking is eliminated, life will return to normal. This may at times occur, but frequently a long readjustment to sobriety is required.

Few marriages are so idyllic as to be without problems, and the partners generally learn how to cope with or resolve these. However, alcoholism so overshadows everything else that all difficulties are attributed to it. The suffering spouse may fantasize how wonderful life would be if only there were no alcohol, and fantasies have a way of being as unrealistic as the classic fairy tale ending, "and they lived happily ever after." When cessation of drinking is not followed by materialization of this fantasy, there is apt to be disappointment, disillusionment, and resentment.

It would be well to compare the alcoholic who stops drinking to a building that has been ruined by fire. Extinguishing the fire does not mean that the building is ready for normal use. There are badly burnt structural beams and fixtures that must be replaced, wiring that must be restored, and walls that need redecorating. The process of restoration may be long, arduous, and expensive. Much the same can be said of the newly recovering alcoholic. The rehabilitation and restoration to normal life may be long and tedious and require a great deal of effort on everyone's part.

First there may be disbelief or lack of trust. The wife is so familiar with the repeated episodes of sobriety that were short-lived, why should this one be different? Even when the alcoholic demonstrates longer abstinence and qualitatively different behavior, such as involvement in treatment and AA, the wife may still feel uneasy about allowing him to resume his position in the household. Having so long demanded that he assume his rightful responsibilities, she may now be quite fearful and reluctant to allow him to do so. The husband may see this hesitation as a "damned if you do and damned if you don't" situation, where there is no way of winning, and the wife may be quite confused in her new dilemma.

It should be remembered that alcohol is a tranquilizer, which is the primary reason for its use. Any tension, anxiety, depression, or other uncomfortable feelings were previously anesthetized by alcohol. It only stands to reason that when the alcoholic discontinues his use of this tranquilizer, his irritability and depression may increase.

Psychologists describe depression as a reaction to a loss. The loss need not necessarily be that of a loved one; it may be loss of one's youth, loss of prestige, or loss of a particular goal. The recovering alcoholic has to deal with a significant loss: the loss of his ability to drink. Where drinking is considered a sign of masculinity, the alcoholic may also feel a loss of his manliness. He may go through a kind of reaction quite similar to that of mourning the death of a loved one. He raises such questions as what he is to do at social affairs when everyone else is drinking, or what he is to say at a business conference when his boss offers him a drink. Even when he recognizes the extreme harmfulness of alcohol to him, he nevertheless maintains an ambivalent attitude, with feelings of longing for the magic elixir.

One of the most complex areas of readjustment is that of sexual relations. Sexuality is a highly sensitive and emotional area because of its intimacy and its importance in the person's identity; also it is apt to present particular difficulty because too often sexual feelings are simply not discussed between husband and wife.

Sexual behavior is profoundly affected during the drinking period. The loss of inhibitions may make the husband more amorous and demanding, whereas the repugnance of the drunkenness may cause the wife to refuse his advances. The rejected alcoholic may become aggressive and even violent, and the traumatized wife may become sexually frigid. The alcoholic may become involved in extramarital affairs. Finally, alcohol may impair sexual performance even to the degree of impotence, and the alcoholic may respond to this threat to his masculinity with more drinking and increased demands.

When recovery begins, the road back to normalization of sexual activity may not be an easy one. The alcoholic may recall his crude behavior while drinking and be so overwhelmed with guilt that he hesitates to make any advances. He may also recall the rejection and not wish to chance another. The wife may not be able to accept sexual intimacy from one who just a short while ago acted as a sex maniac. Or she may actually desire sexual relations and feel deprived if the husband has not resumed his sexual activity. The husband may be impotent or have a fear of impotence, and the anxiety about the latter further impairs his performance. Or the wife may be unable to forgive the extramarital affairs. Any one or more of a myriad of combinations of attitudes toward sex can exist; and since both husband and wife may be hesitant to discuss their sexual feelings frankly with each other, the problem festers and may breed mutual resentment, which increases the distance between them.

The sexual readjustment may require expert counseling, and as early as possible, before additional pathological reactions become deeply ingrained.

Resuming a normal social life may require special efforts. The alcoholic's behavior during the drinking phase may have resulted in loss of any invitations, or the nonalcoholic may have turned down all invitations for fear of an unpleasant scene. Resocialization may require initiative on the part of both the alcoholic and the spouse to reestablish relationships, perhaps by beginning to invite friends to their home. These friends may be curious about what has caused the break in relationships, and generally it is advisable to tell them the truth—which should not be as difficult as it seems, since alcoholism is a poorly kept secret. It is safe to assume that they knew about the drinking, so why not let them know about the recovery?

Sometimes the marriage has deteriorated beyond repair, but the sober spouse nevertheless stays married for the sake of the children. When the alcoholic achieves sobriety, this motivation may no longer be present, and the sober spouse requests separation or divorce. This action can be quite confusing to the alcoholic, who finds his or her recovery rewarded by divorce. The status of the marriage and its viability should be discussed by both partners with the assistance of a trained counselor.

Although any illness, including alcoholism, is a tragic occurrence, it is often noted that people who recover from it attain a strength and depth of character they might not otherwise have reached. Once committed to sobriety, they must take on a degree of honesty and sincerity which the nonalcoholic often transgresses. The soul-searching and efforts at making amends may elevate the recovering alcoholic to a spiritual level superior to that of the nonalcoholic. Continuing growth in sobriety thus can result in considerable growth in character.

The nonalcoholic spouse, so long immersed in the chaos and quagmire of drinking, may breathe a sigh of relief when the nightmare passes and may be quite content to enjoy a normal life. But unless this spouse also grows, he or she may be outpaced by the recovering alcoholic. The previous disparity between the marriage partners may now undergo a reversal, with new sources of dissension. It is not even unheard of for the nonalcoholic spouse to begin drinking excessively when the alcoholic spouse achieves sobriety.

A recovering alcoholic whom I had helped told me once of a recent business venture wherein he had been exploited and abandoned, sustaining a rather significant financial loss. I remarked that I could understand how deeply hurt he was but that I was confident he could overcome it. "I'm sure I can," he said, "but this whole thing has left me with bitter resentments, and I'm on my way to an AA meeting now to help me work my way out of them. You see, I can't afford to harbor resentments, because they are apt to lead me to drinking again."

After this exchange, I began to reflect on whether nonalcoholics recognize the destructiveness of holding onto resentments. Perhaps because their reactions to resentments are not as distinct or dramatic, they may think they are not harmful. However, the lingering hostility and preoccupation with retaliation, whether conscious or unconscious, are unquestionably detrimental. In this case, the recovering alcoholic has the advantage.

One of my acquaintances in AA, with over twenty years of sobriety, begins his talk with the statement, "The man I was drank, and the man I was will drink again." He knows that his personality prior to his drinking was an unhealthy one, which culminated in alcoholism. His recovery consists of becoming someone else. However, his wife did marry the man that was *then*, and the person who emerges from the recovery process is apt to be someone quite different from the man she married. The adjustment to this new person may be a very happy one, but it cannot be taken for granted.

These are just several of the problems that can arise in the recovery process. They and others are not insurmountable but may require dedicated effort and the tripartite approach: counseling or therapy, Alcoholics Anonymous, and Al-Anon.

Bibliography

Berry, Ralph E., Jr., and **Boland, James P.** *The Economic Cost of Alcohol Abuse.* New York: Free Press, 1977.

Burton, Mary. *An Alcoholic in the Family.* Philadelphia: Lippincott, 1974.

Cain, Arthur H. *Alcoholism: Disease or Disgrace.* New York: National Council on Alcoholism, 1959.

Cork, Margaret R. *The Forgotten Children* Toronto: Paper Jacks in Association with Addiction Research Foundation, 1969.

Crosby, John F. *Illusion and Disillusion, The Self In Love and Marriage.* Belmont, Cal.: Wadsworth Publishing Company, 1973.

Crosby, John F., and **Williams, Carl E.** *Choice and Challenge, Contemporary Readings in Marriage.* Dubuque, Iowa: William C. Brown Company. 1974.

Ferber, Andrew, Mendelsohn, Marilyn, and **Napier, Augustus.** *The Book of Family Therapy.* Boston: Houghton Mifflin, 1973.

Fox, Ruth, and **Lyon, Peter.** *Alcoholism: Its Scope, Cause, and Treatment.* New York: Random House, 1955.

Goodwin, Donald. *Is Alcoholism Hereditary?* New York: Oxford University Press, 1976.

Hoff, Curtis E. *Alcoholism: The Hidden Addiction.* New York: Seabury Press, 1974.

Hornik, Edith L. *You and Your Alcoholic Parent.* New York: Association Press, 1974.

Jacobson, George A. *The Alcoholisms.* New York: Human Sciences Press, 1976.

Jellinek, E. M. *The Disease Concept of Alcoholism.* New Haven, Conn.: Hillhouse Press, 1960.

Johnson, Vernon E. *I'll Quit Tomorrow.* New York: Harper and Row, 1973.

Keddie, Nell. *The Myth of Cultural Deprivation.* Middlesex, England: Penguin Books, 1973.

Keller, John E. *Alcohol. A Family Affair. Help for Families in Which There Is Alcohol Misuse.* Santa Ynez, Cal.: The Kroc Foundation, 1977.

Kellerman, Joseph L. *Guide for the Family of the Alcoholic.* New York: Al-Anon Family Group Headquarters, 1962.

Kissin, B., and **Begleiter, H.,** eds. *Social Aspects of Alcoholism.* New York: Plenum Press, 1976.

Laing, R. D. *The Politics of the Family and Other Essays.* New York: Vintage Books, 1969.

Lovell, Harold W. *Hope and Help for the Alcoholic.* New York: Doubleday, 1957.

Lucks, Allan. *Having Been There.* New York: Scribners, 1979.

McCabe, Thomas R. *Victims No More.* Center City, Minn.: Hazelden, 1978.

Mann, Marty. *New Primer on Alcoholism: How People Drink, How to Recognize Alcoholics, and What to Do About Them.* New York: Rinehart and Co., 1958.

Maxwell, Ruth. *The Booze Battle.* New York: Ballantine Books, 1976.

Minuchin, Salvadore. *Families and Family Therapy.* Cambridge, Mass.: Harvard University Press, 1976.

Paolino, Thomas H., Jr., and **McCrady, Barbara.** *The Alcoholic Marriage.* New York: Grune and Stratton, 1977.

S. S. *His Own Enemy.* New Zealand: Blackwood and Janet Paul Auckland, 1965.

Satir, Virginia. *Peoplemaking.* Palo Alto, Cal.: Science and Behavior Books, 1972.

Saxton, Lloyd. *The Individual Marriage, and the Family.* Belmont, Cal.: Wadsworth Publishing Company, 1972.

Seixas, Frank A. *Currents in Alcoholism,* Vol. IV, pp. 15-49. New York: Grune and Stratton, 1977.

Shaw, S., *et al. Responding to Drinking Problems.* Baltimore: University Park Press, 1978.

Twerski, Abraham J. *Like Yourself* *and Others Will, Too.* Englewood Cliffs, N. J.: Prentice-Hall, Inc., 1978.

Index